It's another Quality Book from CGP

This book is for anyone doing WJEC Modular GCSE Mathematics at Higher Level.

It contains lots of tricky questions designed to make you sweat — because that's the only way you'll get any better.

It's also got some daft bits in to try and make the whole experience at least vaguely entertaining for you.

What CGP is all about

Our sole aim here at CGP is to produce the highest quality books — carefully written, immaculately presented and dangerously close to being funny.

Then we work our socks off to get them out to you — at the cheapest possible prices.

Contents

Unit One — Mathematics In Everyday Life

Unit Two — Non-calculator Mathematics

Unit Three — Calculator-allowed Mathematics

Throughout the book, the more challenging questions are marked like this: **Q1**

Published by Coordination Group Publications Ltd.
Illustrated by Ruso Bradley, Lex Ward and Ashley Tyson

From original material by Richard Parsons.

Contributors: Gill Allen, JE Dodds, Mark Haslam, C McLoughlin, John Waller, Dave Williams.

Updated by: Katie Braid, Simon Little, Adam Moorhouse, Jane Towle.

With thanks to Vicky Daniel and Dawn Wright for the proofreading.

ISBN: 978 1 84762 467 3

Groovy website: www.cgpbooks.co.uk
Printed by Elanders Hindson Ltd, Newcastle upon Tyne.
Jolly bits of clipart from CorelDRAW® and VECTOR.

Rounding Numbers

With all these rounding methods, you need to identify the last digit — e.g. if you're rounding 23.41 to 1 decimal place the last digit is 4. Then look at the next digit to the right. If it's 5 or more you round up, if it's 4 or less you round down.

Q1 Round these numbers to the required number of decimal places:

a) 62.1935 (1 dp)
b) 62.1935 (2 dp)
c) 62.1935 (3 dp)
d) 19.624328 (5 dp)
e) 6.2999 (3 dp)
f) π (3 dp)

Q2 Round these numbers to the required number of significant figures.

a) 1329.62 (3 SF)
b) 1329.62 (4 SF)
c) 1329.62 (5 SF)
d) 120 (1 SF)
e) 0.024687 (1 SF)
f) 0.024687 (4 SF)

Remember — the first significant figure is the first digit which isn't zero.

Q3 $K = 456.9873$
Write K correct to:

a) one decimal place
b) two decimal places
c) three decimal places
d) three significant figures
e) two significant figures
f) one significant figure.

Q4 A bumper bag of icing sugar weighs 23.4 kg. What is this correct to the nearest kilogram?

Q5 David divides £15.20 by 3. What is the answer to the nearest penny?

Q6 The great racing driver Speedy Wheelman covered 234.65 miles during the course of one of his races. Give this distance correct to the nearest mile.

Q7 Jack's company pays his travel expenses.
They round the distance he drives to the nearest mile, and then pay 20p for every mile.
In one week, Jack drives 95.45 miles. How much money can Jack claim back?

Q8 A pack of three model cars costs £14.30. John wants to work out what one model car would cost. What is the answer correct to the nearest penny?

Q9 Pru measured the length of her bedroom as 2.345 metres.
Give this measurement correct to the nearest centimetre.

Calculation Bounds

Whenever a measurement is rounded off to a given unit, the actual measurement can be anything up to half a unit bigger or smaller.

1) 90 m to the nearest metre could be anything between 89.5 m and 90.5 m. (But not exactly equal to 90.5 m, or it would be rounded up to 91 m).
2) 700 people to the nearest 10 people could be anything between 695 people and 704 people. (Because this only involves whole numbers.)

Q1 At a golf club, a putting green is given as being 5 m long to the nearest metre. Give the range of values that the actual length of the green could be.

Q2 Carlo weighs himself on some scales that are accurate to the nearest 10 g. The digital display shows his weight as 142.46 kg.

a) What is the maximum that he could weigh?

b) What is the minimum that he could weigh?

Q3 Sandra has a parcel to post. To find out how much it will cost she weighs it.

a) A set of kitchen scales, that weigh to the nearest 10 g, show that the parcel weighs 90 g. Write down the largest weight that the parcel could be.

b) Next she weighs the parcel on a different set of kitchen scales, which are accurate to the nearest 5 g. The packet weighs 95 g. Write down the upper and lower bounds of the weight of the package according to these scales.

c) The post office weighs the parcel on some electronic scales to the nearest gram. It weighs 98 g. Can all the scales be right?

Q4 a) The length of a rectangle is measured as 12 ± 0.1 cm. The width of the same rectangle is measured as 4 ± 0.1 cm. Calculate the perimeter of the rectangle, giving also the maximum possible error.

b) A rectangle measures $A \pm x$ cm in length and $B \pm y$ cm in width. The formula $P = 2(A + B)$ is used to calculate the perimeter, P, of the rectangle. What is the maximum possible error in P?

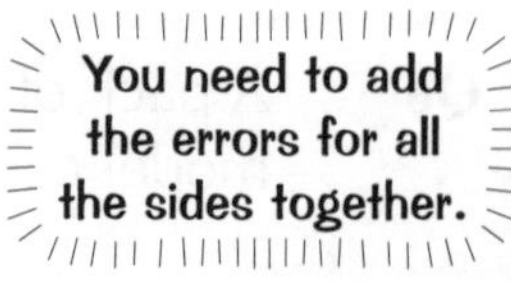

You need to add
the errors for all
the sides together.

Calculation Bounds

Q5 $R = \frac{S}{T}$ is a formula used by stockbrokers.

$S = 940$, correct to 2 significant figures and $T = 5.56$, correct to 3 significant figures.

a) For the value of S, write down the upper bound and the lower bound.
b) For the value of T, write down the upper bound and the lower bound.
c) Calculate the upper bound and lower bound for R.
d) Write down the value of R correct to an appropriate number of significant figures.

Remember — you don't always get the maximum value by using the biggest input values.

Q6 Ash wants to put a new carpet in his living room. He has measured the floor as being 3.4 m × 5.2 m to the nearest 10 cm. What area of carpet should Ash buy to make sure he has enough to cover the whole floor?

Q7 Vince ran a 100 m race in 10.3 seconds. If the time was measured to the nearest 0.1 seconds and the distance to the nearest metre, what is the maximum value of his average speed, in metres per second?

You'll need to use the speed triangle for this question. **See p.8.**

Q8 A lorry travelled 125 kilometres in 1 hour and 50 minutes. If the time was measured to the nearest 10 minutes and the distance to the nearest five kilometres, what was the maximum value of the average speed of the lorry, in kilometres per hour?

Q9 Jimmy, Sarah and Douglas are comparing their best times for running the 1500 m.
Jimmy's best time is 5 minutes 30 seconds measured to the nearest 10 seconds.
Sarah's best time is also 5 minutes 30 seconds, but measured to the nearest 5 seconds.
Douglas' best time is 5 minutes 26 seconds measured to the nearest second.

a) What are the upper and lower bounds for Sarah's best time?
b) Of the three Douglas thinks that he is the quickest at running the 1500 m. Explain why this may not be the case.

Calculator Buttons

Q1 Using the x^2 button on your calculator, work out:

a) 1^2
b) 2^2
c) 11^2
d) 16^2
e) $(-1)^2$
f) 30^2
g) $(-5)^2$
h) 1000^2
i) 0^2

Q2 Using the $\sqrt{\ }$ button on your calculator, work out:

a) $\sqrt{16}$
b) $\sqrt{36}$
c) $\sqrt{289}$
d) $\sqrt{0}$
e) $\sqrt{3600}$
f) $\sqrt{400}$
g) $\sqrt{3}$
h) $\sqrt{7}$
i) $\sqrt{30}$

Q3 Use the $\sqrt[y]{\ }$ button on your calculator to work out:

a) $\sqrt[3]{1}$
b) $\sqrt[3]{0}$
c) $\sqrt[3]{343}$
d) $\sqrt[3]{1000}$
e) $\sqrt[3]{27}$
f) $\sqrt[3]{-27}$
g) $\sqrt[3]{-64}$
h) $\sqrt[3]{-5}$

Yeah, OK, we all know how to do sums on a calculator — but it can do so much more... check out the groovy powers button and the funky brackets buttons, not to mention the slinky 1/x button...

Q4 By calculating the bottom line (the denominator) first and storing it in your calculator, work out:

a) $\dfrac{21}{2+\sqrt{0.25}}$ **b)** $\dfrac{15}{\sqrt[4]{20}+22}$ **c)** $\dfrac{12}{12^2+\sqrt{40}}$

Q5 Using (and), calculate:

Here comes BODMAS...

a) $\dfrac{(14+18)}{(2\times 8)}$
b) $\dfrac{8}{(1\times 4)(8-6)}$
c) $\dfrac{(9+(4\div 2))}{(11\times 3)}$
d) $\dfrac{14(4\times 8)}{(6+9)}$
e) $\dfrac{12}{(8+9)(13-11)}$
f) $\dfrac{7(5+4)}{12(9\times 8)}$

Q6 Using the x^y or ^ button, find:

a) 2^0
b) 4^{10}
c) 2^{20}
d) π^2
e) 2^{-1}
f) 3^{10}
g) 4.29^7

Fractions

The cunning bit with long wordy questions is picking out the important bits and then translating them into numbers. It's not that easy at first, but you'll get better — I guess you've just gotta learn to ignore the waffly stuff.

Q1 What fraction of 1 hour is:
- **a)** 5 minutes
- **b)** 15 minutes
- **c)** 40 minutes?

Q2 If a TV programme lasts 40 minutes, what fraction of the programme is left after:
- **a)** 10 minutes
- **b)** 15 minutes
- **c)** 35 minutes?

Q3 A café employs eighteen girls and twelve boys to wait at tables. Another six boys and nine girls work in the kitchen.
What fraction of the kitchen staff are girls?
What fraction of the employees are boys?

Q4

In a survey, people were asked if they liked a new cola drink. One in five thought it was great, four out of fifteen felt there was no difference in taste, three in ten disliked it and the rest offered no opinion.
What fraction of people offered no opinion?

Q5 Neil wore red trousers on a total of 12 days in November.
- **a)** On what fraction of the total number of days in November did Neil wear red trousers?
- **b)** For 1/5 of the days in November Neil wore a blue shirt. How many days is this?

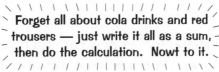

Forget all about cola drinks and red trousers — just write it all as a sum, then do the calculation. Nowt to it.

Q6

The Sandwich Club of Great Britain are going on their annual picnic.
- **a)** The boxes they use to transport their sandwiches are 10 inches high and are the width of a single sandwich. Each sandwich is 5/8 inch thick. How many boxes will they need for 80 sandwiches?
- **b)** How tall would the box need to be if 40 sandwiches were to be stacked inside?

Percentages

A common type of percentage question is working out "something % of something else" — it's dead easy. Just remember to add it back on to the original amount if you've got a VAT question.

Q1 John bought a new TV. The tag in the shop said it cost £299 + VAT.
If VAT is charged at 17½%, how much did he pay (to the nearest penny)?

Q2

Four friends stay at the Pickled Parrot Hotel for a night and each have an evening meal. Bed and Breakfast costs £37 per person and the evening meal costs £15 per person. How much is the total cost, if VAT is added at 17½%?

Q3 The owners of a museum are expecting a 14% increase in visitors next year.
This year they had 20 200 visitors.
How many visitors should they expect next year?

Q4 Donald earns an annual wage of £23 500. He doesn't pay tax on the first £6400 that he earns. How much income tax does he pay a year if the rate of tax is:

a) 25%

b) 40%?

Q5 Tim is choosing between two cars to buy.
The first car is priced at £8495 and has 15% off.
The second car is priced at £8195 and has 12% off.
Which car is the cheapest? Show your working.

Q6 Tanya paid £6500 for her new car. Each year its value decreased by 8%.

a) How much was it worth when it was one year old?

b) How much was it worth when it was two years old?

Q7 Jeremy wanted a new sofa for his lounge. A local furniture shop had just what he was looking for — and for only £130.00 + VAT. Jeremy had £150 pounds in his bank account. If VAT was charged at 17½%, could Jeremy afford the sofa?

Percentages

These questions are about finding "percentage changes" or finding "something as a percentage of something else".

Q8 During a rainstorm, a water butt increased in weight from 10.4 kg to 13.6 kg. What was the percentage increase (to the nearest percent)?

Q9 An electrical store reduces the price of a particular camera from £90.00 to £78.30. What is the percentage reduction?

Q10 There are approximately 6000 fish and chip shops in the UK. On average, a fish and chip shop gets about 160 visitors each day. Given that the population of the UK is roughly 60 million, approximately what percentage of the population visit a fish and chip shop each day?

Q11 At birth, Veronica was 0.3 m tall. By adulthood she had grown to 1.5 m tall. Calculate her height now as a percentage of her height at birth.

Q12 If $L = MN$, what is the percentage increase in L if M increases by 15% and N increases by 20%?

Ooh... another type — finding the original value. The bit most people get wrong is deciding whether the value given represents more or less than 100% of the original — so always check your answer makes sense.

Q13 In the new year sales Robin bought a tennis racket for £68.00. The original price had been reduced by 15%. What was the original price?

Q14 There are 360 people living in a certain village. The population of the village has grown by 20% over the past year.

a) How many people lived in the village one year ago?

b) If the village continues to grow at the same rate, how many whole years from today will it be before the population is more than twice its current size?

Finally, a few questions on percentages and money. Don't be put off by complicated terms like simple and compound interest. Just remember the formulas.

Q15 Tom has sold his mountain bike for £1200 and wants to invest the money in a savings account. An account at Burnley and Brighouse offers compound interest at a rate of 4.5% per year. An account at Natvest offers 5.5% simple interest per year. He plans to leave his money in the account for 4 years. Which is the best account to choose?

Q16 The cash price for a van is £10 000. The van can also be bought on hire purchase for a 20% deposit and 24 monthly payments of £350. What is the hire purchase price?

Speed and Density

The formula for speed is easy enough — and of course you can put it in that good old formula triangle as well.

Average speed = $\frac{\text{Total distance}}{\text{Total time}}$

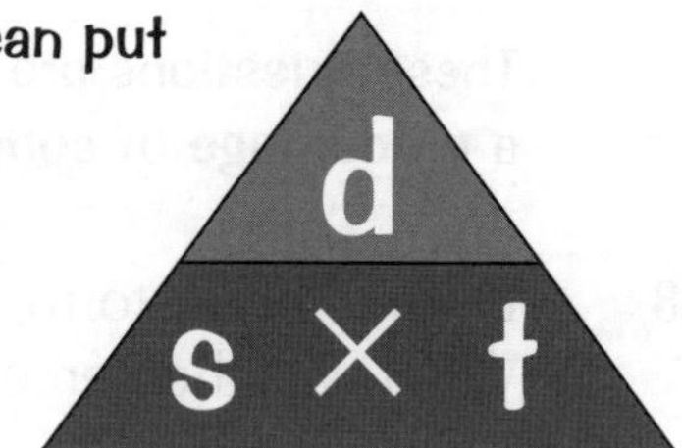

Q1 In a speed trial a sand yacht travelled a measured mile in 36.4 seconds.

a) Calculate this speed in mph.

On the return mile he took 36.16 seconds.

b) Find his total time for the two runs.

c) Calculate the average speed of the two runs in mph.

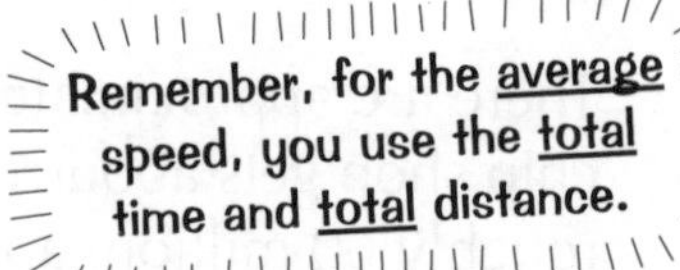

Remember, for the average speed, you use the total time and total distance.

Q2 A motorist drives from Manchester to London. 180 miles is on motorway where he averages 65 mph. 55 miles is on city roads where he averages 28 mph, 15 miles is on country roads where he averages 25 mph.

a) Calculate the total time taken for the journey.

b) How far did he travel altogether?

c) Calculate the average speed for the journey.

Q3 Two athletes run a road race. One ran at an average speed of 16 km/h, the other at 4 m/s. Which was the fastest? How long would each take to run 10 km?

Q4 A plane leaves Amsterdam at 0715 and flies at an average speed of 650 km/h to Paris, arriving at 0800. It takes off again at 0840 and flies at the same average speed to Nice arriving at 1005.

a) How far is it from Amsterdam to Paris?

b) How far is it from Paris to Nice?

c) What was the average speed for the whole journey?

Here we go again — the multi-purpose formula triangle. Learn the positions of M, D and V, plug in the numbers and pull out the answer... magic.

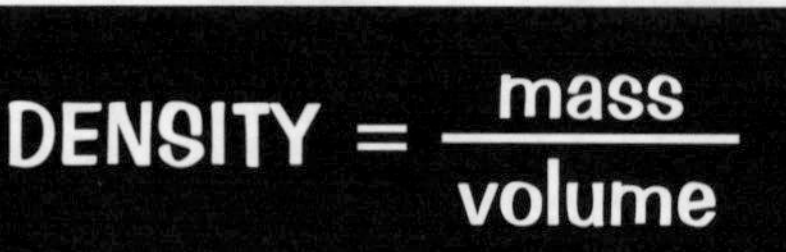

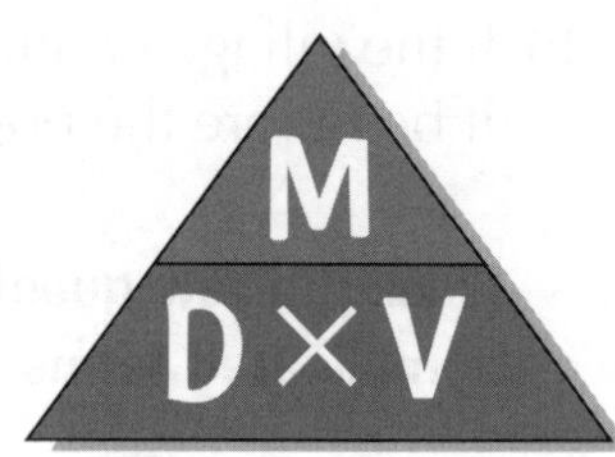

Q5 My copper bracelet has a volume of 3.9 cm^3. The density of copper is 8.9 g/cm^3. Work out the mass of my bracelet.

Q6 Ice has a density of 0.93 g/cm^3. If the mass of a block of ice is 19.5 kg, what is its volume?

Q7 Some petrol in a can has a mass of 4 kg. The density of the petrol is 0.8 g/cm^3. How many litres of petrol are in the can?

1 litre = 1000 cm^3.

Conversion Graphs

Q1 This graph can be used to convert the distance (miles) travelled in a taxi to the fare payable (£). How much will the fare be if you travel:

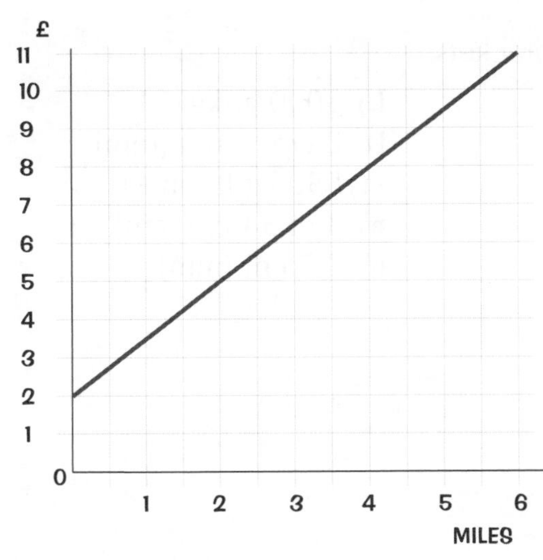

a) 2 miles

b) 5 miles

c) 10 miles

d) Mike lives 4.5 miles away from his friend. Is £16 enough money for Mike to get a taxi to his friend's house and back?

Q2 80 km is roughly equal to 50 miles. Use this information to draw a conversion graph on the grid. Use the graph to estimate the number of miles equal to:

a) 20 km

When you've got to draw your own conversion graph, your best bet is to work out a few different values, and mark them on the graph first.

b) 70 km

c) 90 km

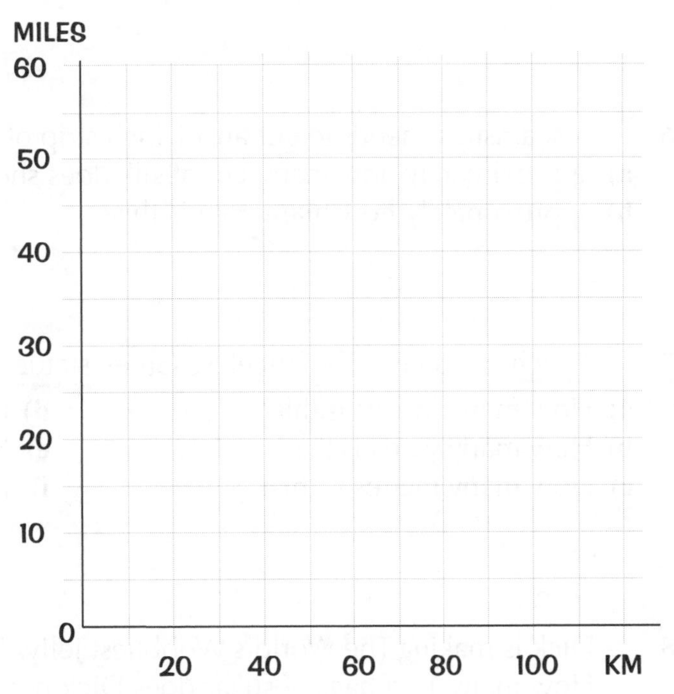

Q3 How many km are equal to:

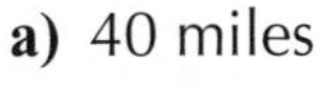

a) 40 miles

b) 10 miles

c) 30 miles

Conversion Factors and Units

You've got to know how to convert between different metric units — there's no way out of it, you'll just have to sit down and learn them, sorry and all that...

Q1 Express the given quantity in the unit(s) in brackets:

a) 2 m [cm]
b) 3.3 cm [mm]
c) 4 kg [g]
d) 600 g [kg]
e) 650 m [km]
f) 9 kg [g]
g) 7 g [kg]
h) 950 g [kg]
i) 6 m [mm]
j) 2 tonnes [kg]
k) 3000 g [kg]
l) 8 cm 6 mm [mm]
m) 550 kg [tonnes]
n) 3 m 54 cm [cm]
o) 0.7 cm [mm]

Q2 Convert 147 kg into pounds.

Q3 A horse's drinking trough holds 14 gallons of water. Given that 1 gallon = 4.5 litres, approximately how many litres can the trough hold?

Q4 Deborah is filling in a health questionnaire. She needs to write down her weight in kilograms. She weighs 9 stone 4 pounds. There are 14 pounds in a stone. How much does Deborah weigh in kilograms?

Q5 Barbara cycled 51 km in one day while Barry cycled 30 miles. Who cycled further?

Q6 A seamstress needs to cut an 11 inch strip of Chinese silk. Given that 1 inch = 2.5 cm,

a) approximately how many cm of silk does she need to cut?
b) approximately how many mm is this?

Q7 1 inch = 2.5 cm. The priceless Greek statue in my garden is 21 feet tall.

a) How many inches is this?
b) How many yards is this?
c) How many metres is this?
d) How many cm is this?
e) How many mm is this?
f) How many km is this?

Q8 Dick is making The World's Wobbliest Jelly. The recipe requires 5 lb of sugar. How many 1 kg bags of sugar does Dick need to buy so that he can make the jelly?

Conversion Factors and Units

Q9 The Bon Voyage Holiday Company are offering an exchange rate of 1.48 euros for £1 sterling. They are also offering 11.03 Danish kroner for £1 sterling and 2.45 Australian dollars for £1 sterling. Calculate, to the nearest penny, the sterling equivalent of:

a) 220 euros
b) 686 Danish kroner
c) 1664 Australian dollars
d) 148 euros
e) 15 Danish kroner
f) 1950 Australian dollars
g) 899 Danish kroner
h) 20 euros
i) 668 Australian dollars
j) 3389 Danish kroner
k) 1000 Australian dollars
l) 1 euro

Q10 At the gym Arnold can lift a barbell weighing 60 kg.
a) Approximately how many lbs is this?
b) How many ounces is this?
Sylvester can lift a barbell weighing 0.059 tonnes.
c) Who can lift the most?

Q11 Justin is shopping online. He looks up the following exchange rates:

1.60 US Dollars ($) to £1 Sterling.

150 Japanese Yen (¥) to £1 Sterling.

Calculate to the nearest penny the cost in Sterling of each of Justin's purchases:
a) A book costing $7.50
b) An MP3 player costing ¥7660

Q12 Simon is on holiday in Cyprus. He wants to compare the price of beer there with the price he pays at home. He knows the following conversion rates.

£1 = €1.48 1 pint = 0.568 litres

A pint of beer in his local pub costs £2.15.
A litre of beer in the poolside bar at his hotel costs €4.00.
Which is better value?

Q13 Neil is going to buy some fabric for a new pair of trousers that he is going to make. A local shop prices the fabric that he would like at £9.84 per square yard. A fabric superstore prices the same fabric at £10.80 per square metre. According to price, where should Neil buy his fabric? (Use the conversion factor 1 m = 1.1 yard.)

Scale Drawings and Bearings

Q1 The scale on a map is 1:10 000.
How big are the following in real life:
a) a distance of 2 cm on the map
b) a distance of 20 cm on the map
c) a distance of 70 cm on the map
d) an area of 2 cm^2 on the map?

Maps can be tricky. Best thing is to keep the units the same when you do the initial conversion, then do another conversion to the appropriate units.

Q2 Another map has a scale of 1:3000.
What size on this map are the following:
a) a distance of 5 km in real life
b) a distance of 1 km in real life
c) an area of 100 m^2 in real life
d) an area of 50 m^2 in real life?

Just remember — the distance on the map is unlikely to be larger than the real-life distance.

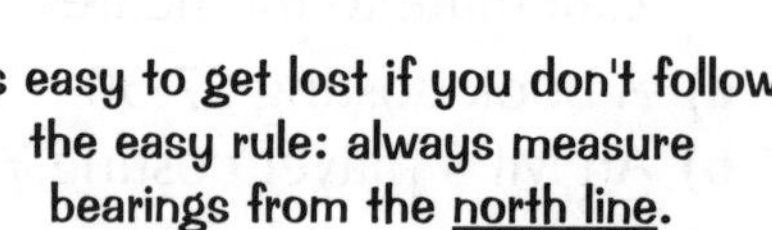

It's easy to get lost if you don't follow the easy rule: always measure bearings from the north line.

Q3 Find the bearings required in these diagrams.

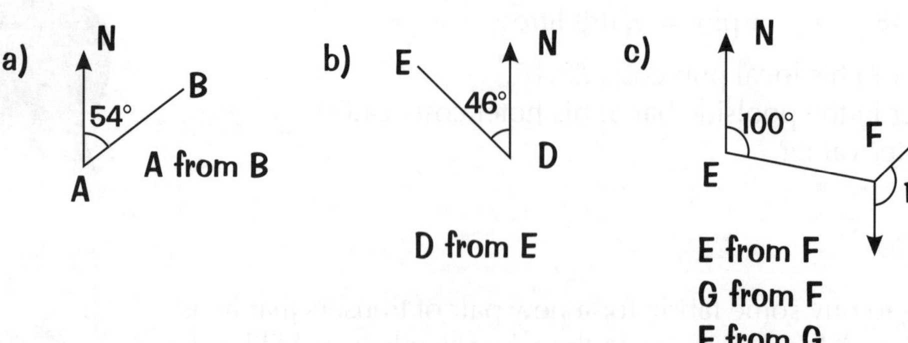

Perimeter and Area

Q1 Calculate the area and perimeter of the rectangle.

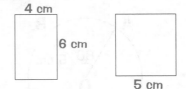

Q2 Calculate the area and perimeter of the square.

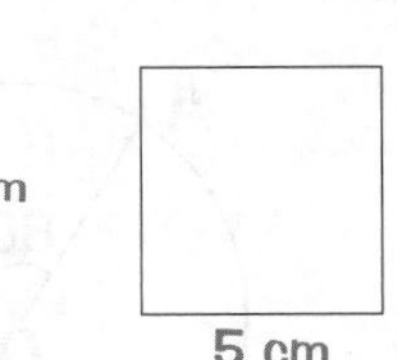

Q3 You have been asked to paint the outside wall of a building shown in the diagram opposite.
a) Find the area of wall that needs painting.
b) A 1 litre tin of paint will cover 13 m^2. How many 1 litre tins are needed to give the wall two coats of paint?
c) The wall is also going to have a tiled border around the edge. Calculate the length of the edge of the wall to be tiled.

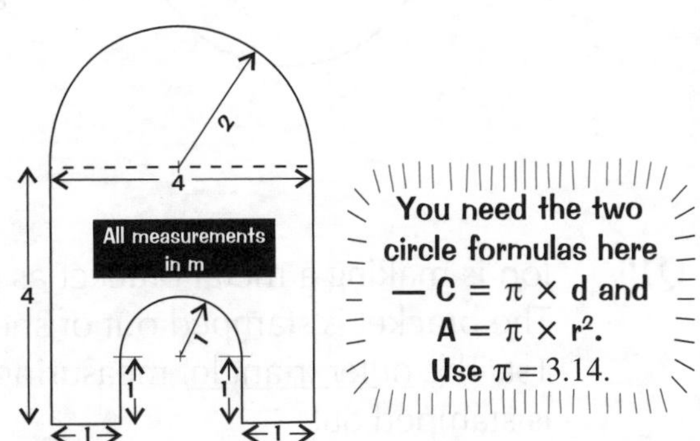

Q4 A rectangular dining room, with a width equal to half its length, needs carpet tiling.
a) Calculate the area of the floor, if its width is 12 m.
b) If carpet tiles are 50 cm by 50 cm squares, calculate how many tiles will be required.
c) If carpet tiles cost £4.99 per m^2, calculate the cost of tiling the dining room.

Q5 An attachment on a child's toy is made from plastic in the shape of an octagon with a square cut out. By counting squares or otherwise, find the area of plastic needed to make 4 of these attachments.

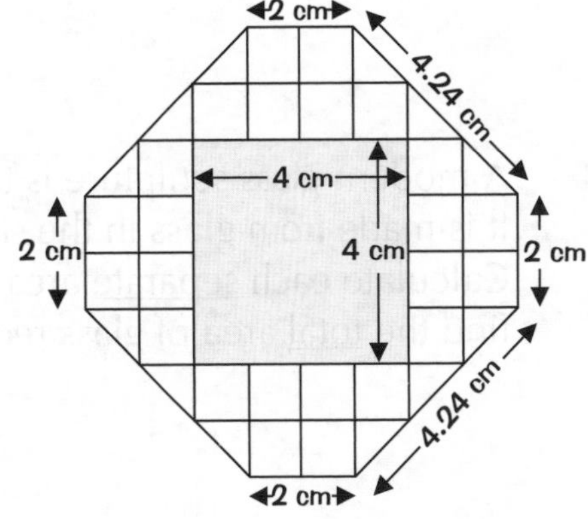

Q6 Josh is making a cube bean bag out of material for his textiles coursework. If each side of the cube is to have edges of length 60 cm, how many square metres of material will Josh need?

Q7 Natasha is training for a marathon by jogging around the outside of a square field of area 9000 m^2. One evening, Natasha completed 11 laps of the field. How far did she run? Give your answer to the nearest 100 m.

Q8 Find the area and the perimeter of each of the shapes drawn here. Use $\pi = 3.14$.

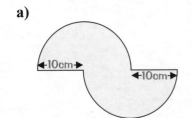

a)

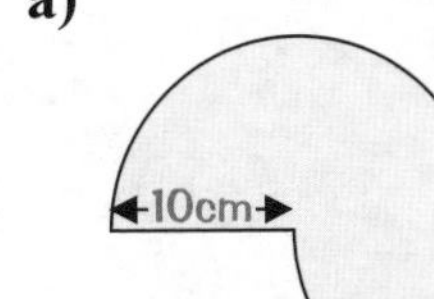

b)

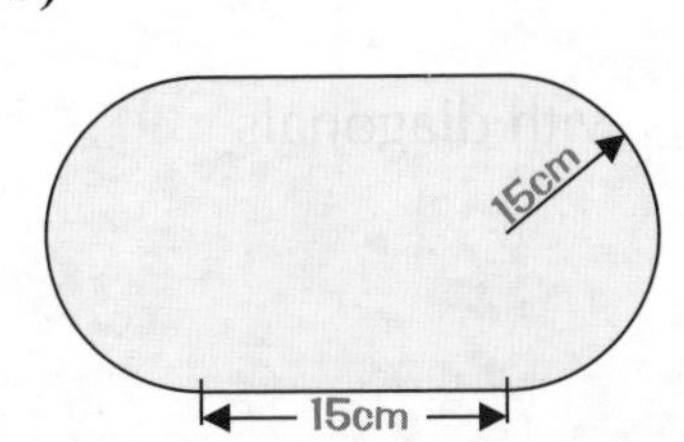

c)

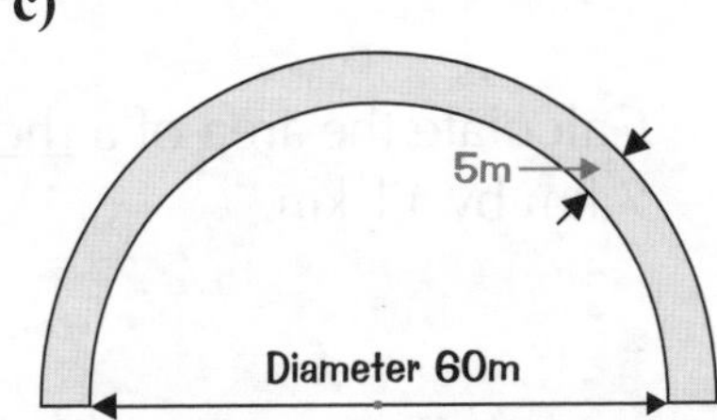

Perimeter and Area

Q9

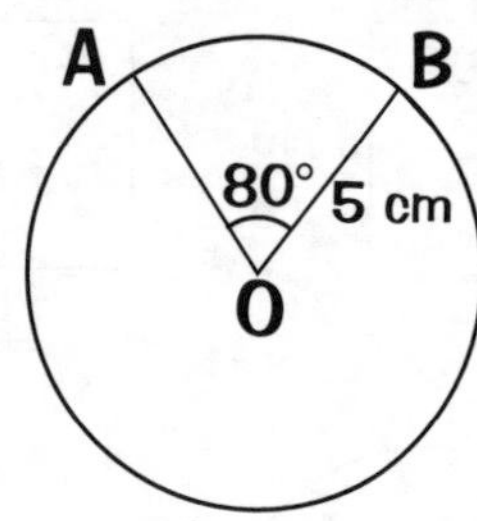

A piece of cheese viewed from the top looks like a circle. The circle has radius 5 cm and the angle AOB = 80°.
Find the area of the top of the slice shown by the sector OAB.

Q10 Jon is making a metal bracket as part of his technology project. The bracket is stamped out of sheet metal in a 2 phase process:
1st: The <u>outer triangle</u>, measuring 14.4 cm by 10 cm, is stamped out.
2nd: A smaller <u>inner triangle</u> measuring 5.76 cm by 4 cm is stamped out of the larger triangle.
The bracket should be made from no more than 50 cm^2 of sheet metal if the fixing is to support its weight.
Will the fixing take the weight of Jon's bracket?

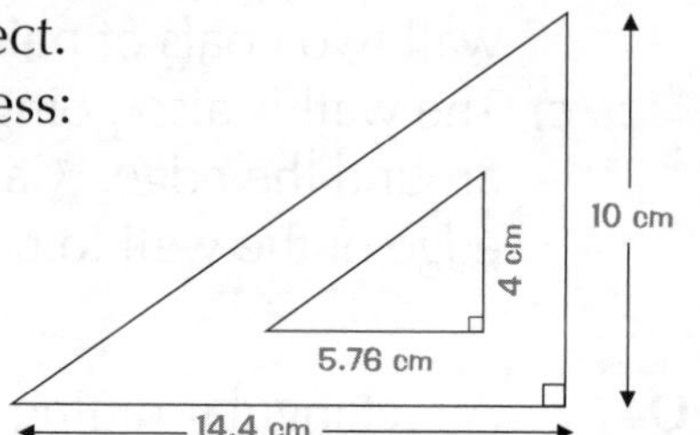

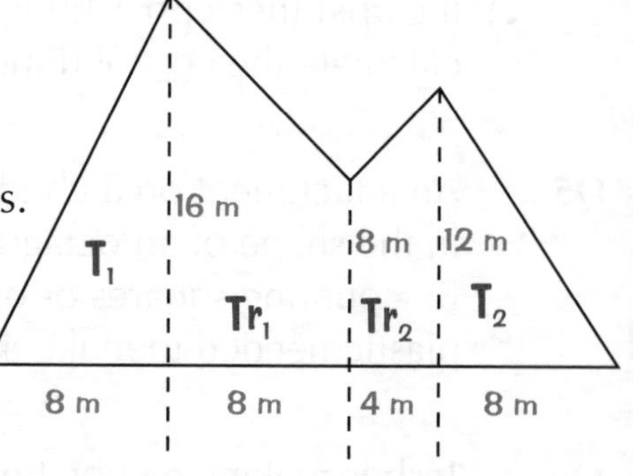

Q11 A modern glass sculpture is to be erected. It is made from glass in the shape of two mountain peaks. Calculate each <u>separate</u> area and hence find the <u>total</u> area of glass required.

Q12 A simple tent is to be made in the shape of a triangular prism. The dimensions are shown in the diagram.

a) The two end faces are isosceles triangles. Find their areas.

b) The two sides and ground sheet are rectangles. Find their areas.

c) How much material is required to make this tent?

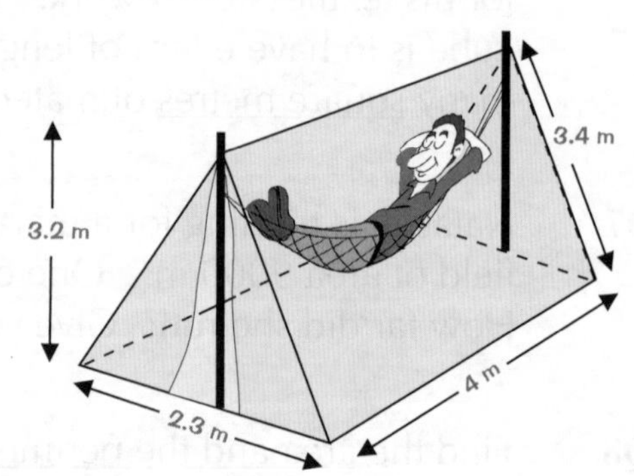

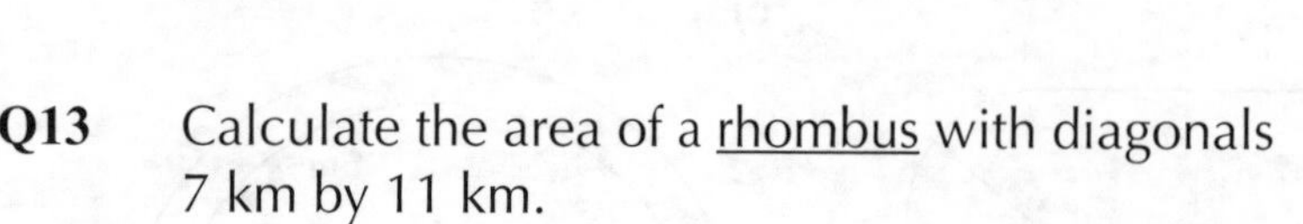

Q13 Calculate the area of a <u>rhombus</u> with diagonals 7 km by 11 km.

Volume

Make sure you know the <u>5 main volume formulas</u> — for <u>cuboids</u>, <u>prisms</u>, <u>pyramids</u>, <u>cones</u> and <u>spheres</u>.

Q1 Joe buys a polythene tunnel to protect his plants from frost. It has a semicircular diameter of 70 cm and a length of 3 m.

a) Find the cross-sectional area.

b) Hence find the volume of the tunnel.

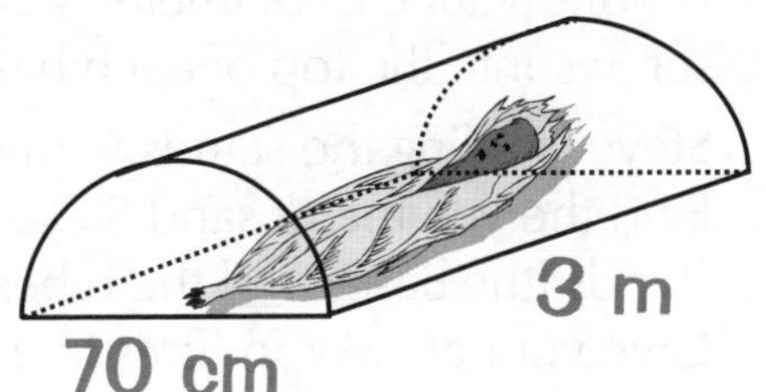

Q2 I am planning to build a circular pond in my garden surrounded by a ring shaped paved area. The pond will be 50 cm deep and filled with water.

a) Calculate the approximate cost of paving the area around the pond with slabs costing £16 per m^2. Give your answer to the nearest £10.

b) I need to add 15 ml of liquid pond treatment for every m^3 of water in the pond. Find the volume of treatment I will need to add to the pond. Give your answer to the nearest ml.

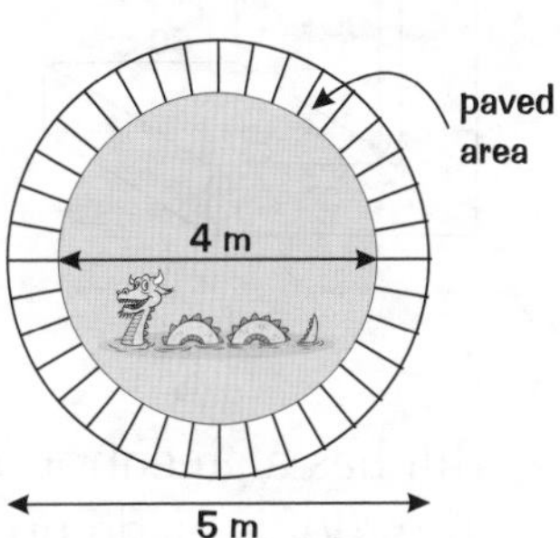

Q3 A solid metal cube, each of whose sides is 10 cm long, is melted down and made into a solid cylinder 10 cm high.

a) What is the radius of this cylinder?

b) Find the surface area of the cylinder.

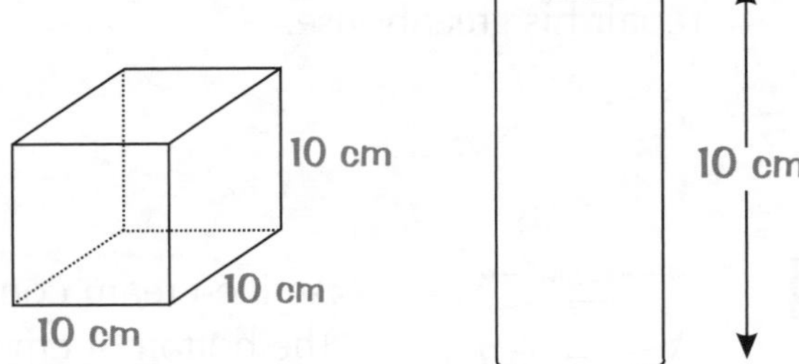

Q4 A tin mug has the dimensions shown.

a) What is the greatest volume of milk the mug can hold?

b) In fact, 600 cm^3 of milk is poured in. How high will it go up the mug?

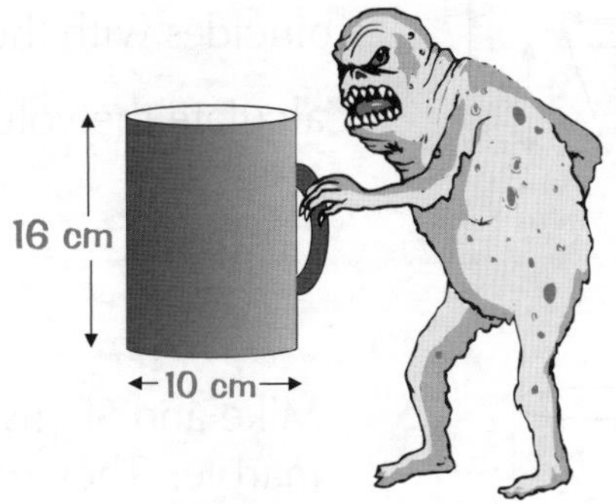

Q5

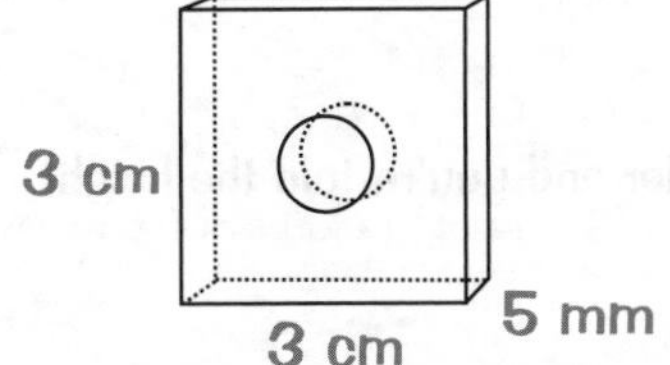

A nut has the cross-section illustrated. The circular hole has a diameter of 1.4 cm and the nut is 5 mm thick. Find the volume of the nut in cm^3.

Volume

Q6 Steve has bought a pair of speaker stands. The base of each stand is a hollow prism with the dimensions shown. A hollow tube of diameter 4 cm and height 110 cm screws into the top of each base to form the stand.

Steve is filling the stands with sand to improve stability. Find the volume of sand Steve needs to use to fill both stands (the bases <u>and</u> the tubes). Give your answer in litres to 2 d.p.

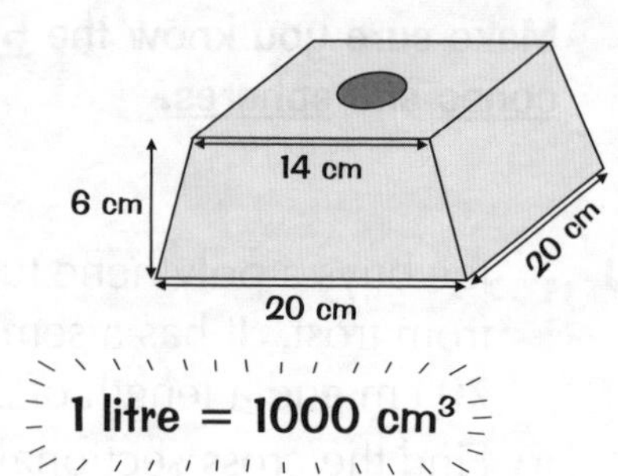

Q7

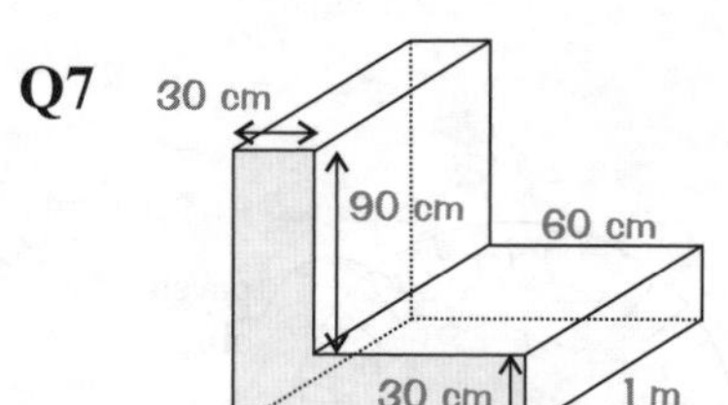

Jill buys a bookshelf with the dimensions shown in the diagram.

a) Find the cross-sectional area.

b) Find the volume of the bookshelf in m³.

Q8 Bill has a greenhouse with dimensions as shown. The roof is made up of eight panels of equal size.

A storm breaks all of the glass in the shaded area on the diagram.

Calculate the area of glass which Bill must buy to repair his greenhouse.

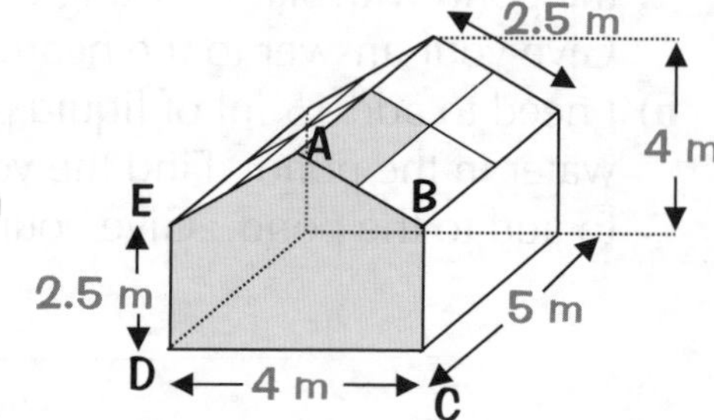

Q9

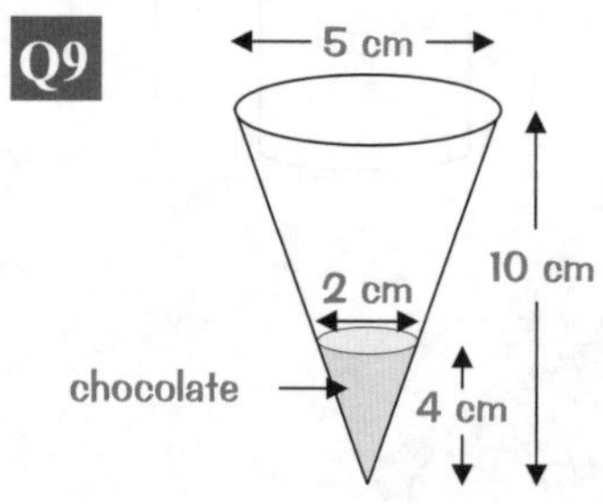

An ice-cream cone is 10 cm deep and has a base diameter of 5 cm. The bottom 4 cm of the cone is filled with solid chocolate as shown. The rest of the cone is filled with ice cream and a hemisphere of ice cream is mounted on top so that the base of the hemisphere coincides with the base of the cone.

Calculate the volume of ice cream required to make one ice cream.

Q10

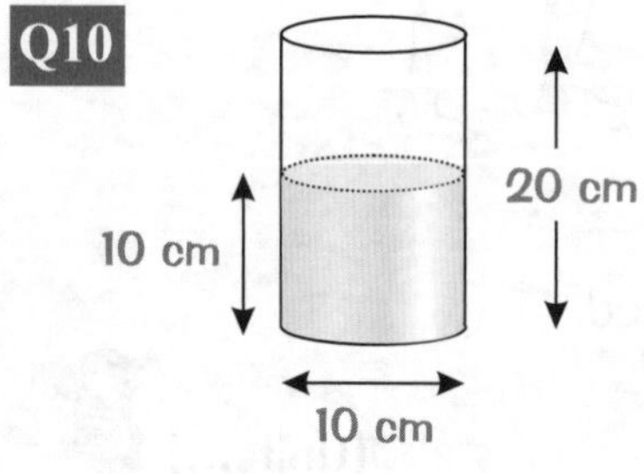

Mike and Shelly are doing an experiment to find the radius of a marble. They fill a cylindrical container of diameter 10 cm and height 20 cm with water to a depth of 10 cm. 200 identical marbles are now submerged in the water. The depth increases to 14.5 cm. Calculate the radius of one marble.

The volume increase is a cylinder and you're told the height.

Collecting Data

Q1 Stanley is researching the use of the school canteen.
He asks this question to a sample of students at the school:

How often do you use the canteen? Tick one of the boxes.

Very often ☐ **Quite often** ☐

Not very often ☐ **Never** ☐

a) Give one criticism of Stanley's question.

b) Write a question that Stanley could use to find out how often students use the canteen.

Q2 A local council wants to find out how they can attract businesses to their area.
They design a questionnaire which includes this question:

How many employees at your company watch soap operas?

Give one criticism of this question.

Q3 Decide if each of the following questions are suitable for a survey to find which of five desserts (cheesecake, fruit salad, sherry trifle, knickerbocker glory and chocolate cake) people like the most. Give a reason for each of your answers.

a) Do you like cheesecake, fruit salad, sherry trifle, knickerbocker glory or chocolate cake?

b) How often do you eat dessert?

c) Which is your favourite out of: cheesecake; fruit salad; sherry trifle; knickerbocker glory; chocolate cake?

d) What is your favourite dessert?

e) Is your favourite dessert: cheesecake; fruit salad; sherry trifle; knickerbocker glory; chocolate cake; none of these?

Q4 Pauline is the manager of a small café. She knows that some of her customers buy cold drinks from the cold drinks machine, some buy hot drinks from the hot drinks machine and some people buy snacks and drinks at the counter.
Pauline would like to use a questionnaire to find out whether she should stock a new brand of cola. Here is part of Pauline's questionnaire:

Café Questionnaire

1) Please tick the box to show how often you visit the cafe:

daily ☐ **weekly** ☐ **fortnightly** ☐ **monthly** ☐ **less than monthly** ☐

a) Using the same style, design another question that Pauline can include in her questionnaire.

b) Pauline hands out her questionnaire as she serves customers at the counter.
Give a reason why this is a suitable or unsuitable way to hand out the questionnaire.

Mean, Median, Mode and Range

For finding the mode and median put the data in order of size — it's much easier to find the most frequent and middle values.

The mean involves a bit more calculation, but hey, you're doing maths...

Q1 The local rugby team scored the following number of tries in their first 10 matches of the season:

3	5	4	2	0	1	3	0	3	4

Find their modal number of tries.

Q2 Find the mean, median, mode and range of these numbers:

1	2	–2	0	1	8	3	–3	2	4	–2	2

Q3 A company has 9 employees in the sales department who earn commission. They are advertising for another salesperson and want to say in the advert how much commission their staff earn on average. The amount of commission the 9 existing salespeople earned last year is as follows:

£13,000	£9,000	£7,500
£18,000	£12,000	£7,500
£23,000	£15,000	£11,500

a) Find the mean, median and mode of their earnings.
b) Which one does not give a good indication of their average commission?
c) Which should the company put in the advert, and why?

Q4 Molly is writing a letter of complaint to the bus company because she thinks her bus to school is regularly late. Over 3 weeks, Molly kept a record of how many minutes her bus was either early or late, and put this in her letter. (She used + for late and – for early.)

+2	–1	0	+5	–4
–7	0	–8	0	+4
–4	–3	+14	+2	0

a) Calculate the mean lateness/earliness of the bus.
b) Calculate the median.
c) What is the mode?
d) The bus company use the answers to **a), b)** and **c)** to claim they are always on time. Is this true?

Careful with this — you have to use the averages to find the total weight, then divide to find the new average.

Q5 The average weight of the 11 players in a football team was 72.5 kg. The average weight of the 5 reserve players was 75.6 kg. What was the average weight of the whole squad? (Give your answer to 3 s.f.)

Q6 The mean daily weight of potatoes sold in a greengrocer's from Monday to Friday was 14 kg. The mean daily weight of potatoes sold from Monday to Saturday was 15 kg. How many kg of potatoes were sold on Saturday?

Mean, Median, Mode and Range

Q7 Colin averaged 83% over 3 exams. His average for the first two exams was 76%. What was Colin's score in the final exam?

Q8 The range for a certain list of numbers is 26, one of the numbers in the list is 48.
a) What is the lowest possible value a number in the list could be?
b) What is the highest possible value that could be in the list?

Q9 An ordinary dice is rolled 6 times, landing on a different number each time.
a) What is the mean score?
b) What is the median score?
c) What is the range of scores?

Q10 The bar graph shows the amount of time Jim and Bob spend watching TV during the week.

a) Find the mean amount of time per day each spends watching TV.

b) Find the range of times for each of them.

c) Using your answers from **a)** and **b)**, comment on what you notice about the way they watch TV.

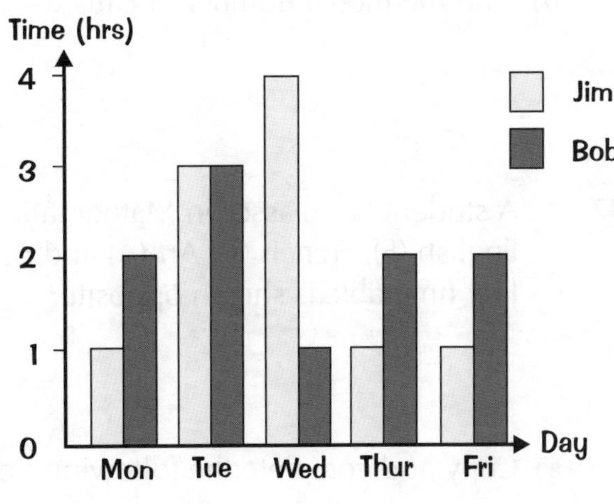

Q11 Mr Jones posted 88 Christmas cards first class on Monday. His friends received them over the week: 40 on Tuesday, 28 on Wednesday, 9 on Thursday, 6 on Friday and the remainder on Saturday.
a) Find the modal number of days it took for the cards to arrive.
b) Find the median number of days it took for the cards to arrive.
c) "The majority of first class post arrives within 2 days." Is the above statement true or false in the light of the data?

Q12 In each of the following cases, decide which average is referred to:
a) this average is least appropriate when the total number of values is small
b) this average is least affected if one of the values is removed at random
c) this average is most affected by the presence of extreme values.

Frequency Tables

You've got to be able to do these in both row and column form, because they could give you either one. There's no real difference, and the rules are still the same.

Q1 To monitor their annual performance, a travel company logs all calls to their sales desk. The number of calls per day received by the sales desk over a given year are shown here.

No. of Calls	10	11	12	13	14	15	16 and over
No. of Days	110	70	120	27	18	12	8

a) Find the median number of calls.
b) Find the modal number of calls.

Q2 A student has classes in Mathematics (M), English (E), French (F), Art (A) and Science (S). Her timetable is shown opposite.

Monday	S S E E A
Tuesday	E M M A A
Wednesday	S M E F F
Thursday	F E E A S
Friday	M M E S S

a) Copy and complete the following frequency table for a week's lessons:

Subject	M	E	F	A	S
Frequency					

b) Calculate the number of French lessons that the student will attend during a 12-week term.

c) What is the modal lesson?

Q3 20 pupils are asked to estimate the length (to the nearest m) of their gardens. Here are the results: 10, 8, 6, 4, 10, 8, 0, 14, 12, 8, 10, 6, 1, 6, 10, 8, 6, 6, 8, 8
Copy the frequency table below and put the estimates in.

Length (m)	4 and under	6	8	10	12	14 and over
Frequency						

a) Find the mode of the data.
b) Find the median of the data.
c) State the range of the data.

Frequency Tables

Q4 130 female bus drivers were weighed to the nearest kg.
Calculate:
a) the median weight
b) the modal weight
c) the mean weight, by first completing the table.

Weight (kg)	Frequency	Weight × Frequency
51	40	
52	30	
53	45	
54	10	
55	5	

Q5 A football magazine rates teams according to how many goals they're likely to score in a match, based on their last 20 matches. The table below shows the number of goals scored by Spark Bridge Wanderers over this period.

No. of goals	0	1	2	3	4	5	6
Frequency	0	1	1	7	6	3	2

Find the mean, mode and median of the data.

Q6 A tornado has struck the hamlet of Moose-on-the-Wold. Many houses have had windows broken. The frequency table shows the devastating effects.

No. of windows broken per house	0	1	2	3	4	5	6
Frequency	5	3	4	11	13	7	2

a) Calculate the modal number of broken windows.
b) Calculate the median number of broken windows.
c) Calculate the mean number of broken windows.

Q7 Using the computerised till in a shoe shop, the manager can predict what stock to order from the previous week's sales.
Opposite is the tabulated printout for <u>last week</u> for <u>men's shoes</u>.

Shoe size	5	6	7	8	9	10	11
frequency	9	28	56	70	56	28	9

a) The mean, mode and median for this data can be compared. For each of the following statements decide whether it is true or false.
i) The <u>mode</u> for this data is <u>70</u>.
ii) The <u>mean</u> is <u>greater than</u> the <u>median</u> for this distribution.
iii) The mean, median and mode are <u>all equal</u> in this distribution.

b) What <u>percentage</u> of customers bought shoes of the <u>mean size</u> from last week's sales data:

i) 30% **ii)** 70% **iii)** 0.273% or **iv)** 27.3%?

Charts and Graphs

Q1 One hundred vehicles on a road were recorded as part of a traffic study. Use this two-way table to answer the following questions.

	Van	Motor-bike	Car	Total
Travelling North	15			48
Travelling South	20		23	
Total		21		100

a) How many vans were recorded?

b) How many vehicles in the survey were travelling south?

c) How many motorbikes were travelling south?

d) How many cars were travelling north?

Q2 The grading for skiers to be awarded certificates is as follows:
B - beginner, I - intermediate, G - good, VG - very good, R - racer.

To clarify the situation for a school group travelling to the Alps, the ski company would like a table and a chart to show the information as clearly as possible.

B	I	B	I	R	VG	I
I	R	G	VG	VG	B	B
I	I	B	B	R	B	G
I	B	G	G	I	I	I

a) What sort of table can you suggest? Draw it accurately.

b) What sort of chart can you suggest? Draw it accurately.

c) What is the most common type of skier?

Q3 Having seen the line graph opposite, a Quality Control Manager said "Admittedly we do have some complaints about our products, but from July complaints have tailed off, so our products must be of a better quality."
From the graph, do you think this statement is correct? Why/Why not?

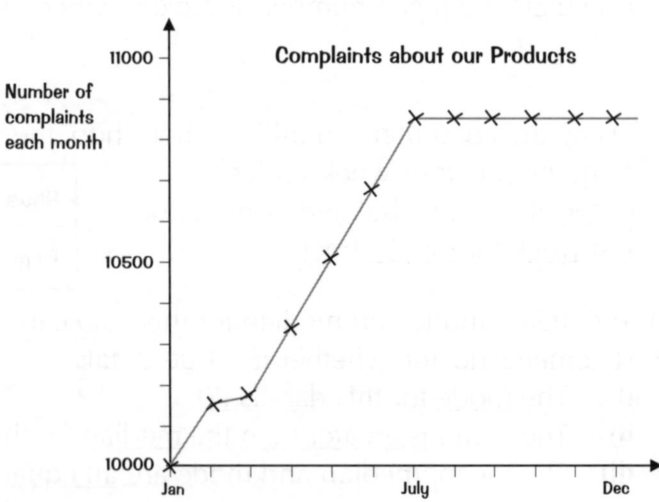

Pie Charts

Everyone loves a pie chart. Oh, no, sorry, that's pies...

When constructing a pie chart, follow the three steps:

1) Add up the numbers in each sector to get the TOTAL.
2) Divide 360° by the TOTAL to get the MULTIPLIER.
3) Multiply EVERY number by the MULTIPLIER to get the ANGLE of each SECTOR.

Q1 A company that makes and sells pies wants to add a nutritional information diagram to their packaging. Construct a pie chart using the template on the right, to show the following nutritional data for one of their pies:

Contents of Pie	Amount per 100 g
Carbohydrate	35 g
Protein	15 g
Fat	10 g
Magical fairy dust	40 g

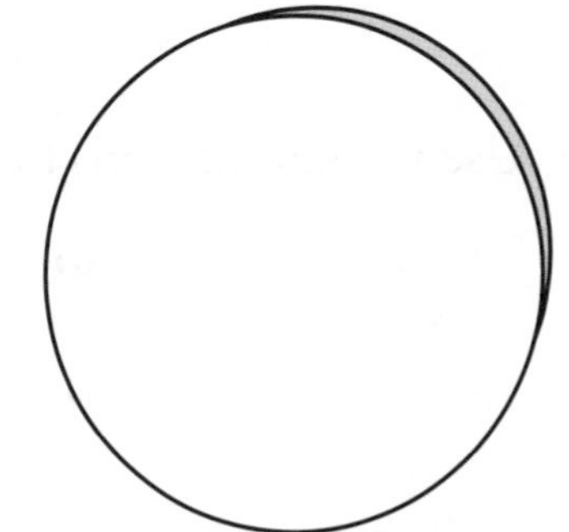

Q2 According to the tourist board for the Hindle Isles, 380,000 people visited the biggest island in the group, Sherrington, in 2009. The distribution of tourists for the whole group of islands is shown in the pie chart. Use a protractor on the diagram to find the number of tourists visiting the other islands in 2009 (rounded to the nearest 10,000).

Use the info you're given to find the number of tourists represented by 1°.

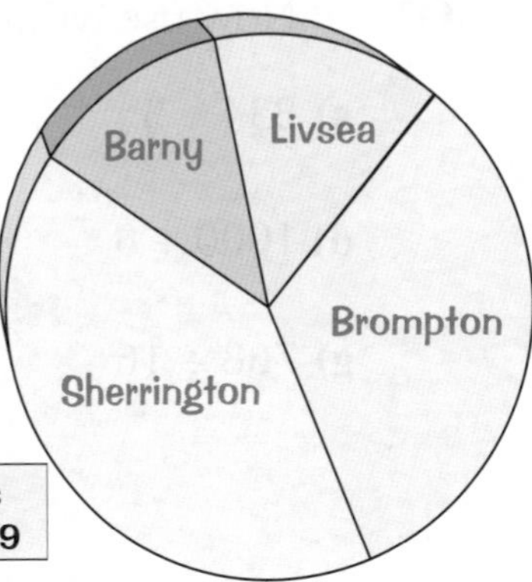

The distribution of visitors to the Hindle Isles in 2009

Q3 The pie chart shows the results of a survey of forty 11 year olds when asked what their favourite vegetable is with Sunday lunch. Which one of the following may be deduced from the information in the pie chart?

2 peas
5 potatoes
Don't eat vegetables
10 roast potatoes
3 carrots
1 cauliflower

a) Potatoes are the least popular vegetable.
b) 3/4 of the children like potatoes of some type.
c) 1/10 of the children like carrots or cauliflower.
d) 11/40 of the children asked what their favourite vegetable is, replied "Don't eat vegetables."

Q4 The pie charts opposite appear in a newspaper article about a local election. Nicki says that more people voted for the Green party in 2009 than in 2005.

Comment on whether it's possible to tell this from the pie charts.

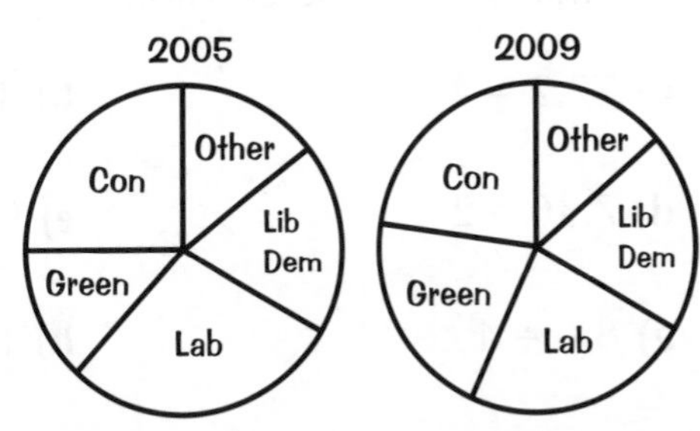

Written Multiplication and Division

NO CALCULATORS for any of the questions in this section.

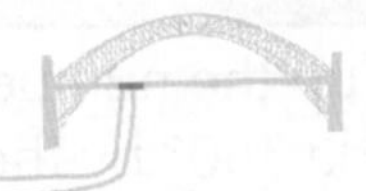

Time to test your multiplying and dividing skills without a calculator. There are lots of methods — you need to pick a method you like and practise using it on questions until it's as stress free as bungee jumping...

Q1 Use written methods to multiply the following:

a) 23 × 2 **b)** 225 × 3 **c)** 546 × 5 **d)** 126 × 14

e) 152 × 33 **f)** 413 × 26 **g)** 309 × 61 **h)** 847 × 53

Q2 Now use written methods to deal with these:

a) 834 ÷ 3 **b)** 645 ÷ 5 **c)** 702 ÷ 6

d) 1000 ÷ 8 **e)** 595 ÷ 17 **f)** 728 ÷ 13

g) 768 ÷ 16 **h)** 996 ÷ 24 **i)** 665 ÷ 14

Now let's try some slightly trickier questions involving decimals.

Q3 Now try these multiplications.

a) 6.2 × 4 **b)** 8.6 × 5

c) 4.75 × 3 **d)** 66.2 × 0.2

e) 263 × 1.4 **f)** 2.52 × 0.13

Count the number of d.p.s in the question and put the same number into your answer.

Q4 Finally, try these divisions:

a) 27.2 ÷ 4 **b)** 31.8 ÷ 6 **c)** 52.15 ÷ 7

d) 7.36 ÷ 2 **e)** 91.2 ÷ 3 **f)** 37.8 ÷ 14

g) 8.6 ÷ 4 **h)** 117.6 ÷ 7 **i)** 156.8 ÷ 4

Estimating

Q1 Find approximate answers to the following:

a) 6560×1.97
b) 8091×1.456
c) $38.45 \times 1.4237 \times 5.0002$
d) $45.34 \div 9.345$
e) $34504 \div 7133$
f) $\frac{55.33 \times 19.345}{9.23}$
g) 7139×2.13
h) $98 \times 2.54 \times 2.033$
i) $21 \times 21 \times 21$
j) $8143 \div 81$
k) $62000 \div 950$
l) $\pi \div 3$

Turn these into nice easy numbers that you can deal with without a calculator.

Q2 At the start of the week, a shop had approximately 15 000 cartons of broccoli juice in stock. The shop sold 1483 cartons on Monday, 2649 on Tuesday, 1539 on Wednesday, 1478 on Thursday and 2958 on Friday. Estimate the number of cartons remaining.

Q3 Estimate the area under the graph.

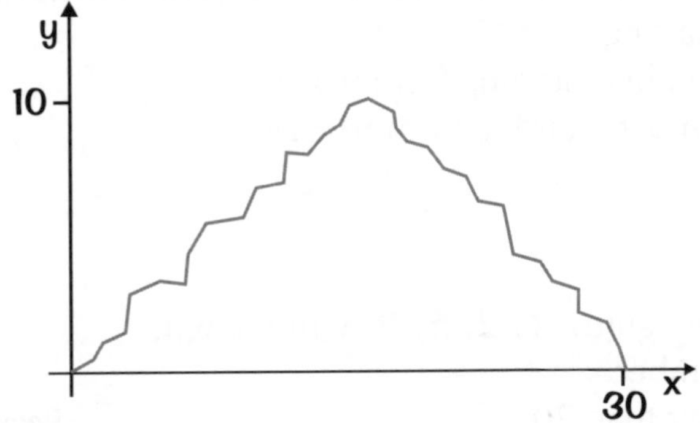

Q4 A supermarket chain sold 1463 tins of beans during a four week period.
a) If the supermarkets were open every day of the week, how many days did it take to sell the 1463 tins of beans?
b) Estimate the average number of tins sold each day. Show your working.

Q5 Joan needs to estimate the size of her bedroom so that she can buy enough paint to cover the walls. Two of the walls measure 2.86 m by 3.16 m, and the other two walls measure 2.86 m by 3.42 m.
a) Estimate the area that Joan needs to paint in m².
b) If one tin of paint will cover 15 m², how many tins of paint will Joan need to paint her bedroom?

Q6 Mark wants to buy some tropical fish. The pet shop owner tells him that he will need a tank with a volume of at least 7000 cm³. Estimate whether Mark's tank will be big enough.

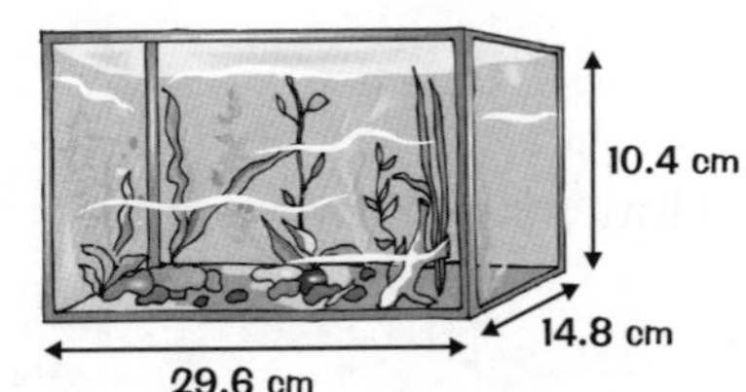

Types of Number

There are a few special number sequences that you really need to know — SQUARE, CUBE and PRIME NUMBERS, as well as POWERS and ODD and EVEN NUMBERS.

Q1 Sarah thinks of a number. She calculates that the square of the number is 81. What is the square root of the number?

Q2 1 is the first odd number. It is also the first square number and the first cube number. Which is greater: the third odd number, the third square number or the third cube number?

Q3 The following sequences are described in words. Write down their first four terms.
- **a)** The prime numbers starting from 17.
- **b)** The squares of odd numbers starting from $9^2 = 81$.
- **c)** The cubes of even numbers starting from $6^3 = 216$.

Q4 Using any or all of the figures **1, 2, 5, 9** write down:
- **a)** the smallest prime number
- **b)** a prime number greater than 20
- **c)** a prime number between 10 and 20
- **d)** two prime numbers whose sum is 21
- **e)** a number that is not prime.

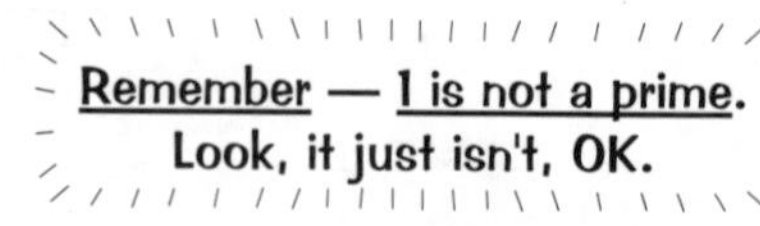

Remember — 1 is not a prime.
Look, it just isn't, OK.

Q5 a) In the ten by ten square opposite, ring all the prime numbers. (The first three have been done for you.)
- **b)** Among the prime numbers between 10 and 100, find three which are still prime when their digits are reversed.
- **c)** Give a reason for 27 not being a prime number.

1	(2)	(3)	4	(5)	6	7	8	9	10
11	12	13	14	15	16	17	18	19	20
21	22	23	24	25	26	27	28	29	30
31	32	33	34	35	36	37	38	39	40
41	42	43	44	45	46	47	48	49	50
51	52	53	54	55	56	57	58	59	60
61	62	63	64	65	66	67	68	69	70
71	72	73	74	75	76	77	78	79	80
81	82	83	84	85	86	87	88	89	90
91	92	93	94	95	96	97	98	99	100

Q6 How many prime numbers are even?

Multiples, Factors and Prime Factors

Q1 1 3 6 9 12

From the numbers above, write down:

a) a multiple of 4
b) the prime number
c) two square numbers
d) three factors of 27
e) two numbers, P and Q, that satisfy both $P = 2Q$ and $P = \sqrt{144}$

This is real basic stuff — you just have to know your times tables. And your primes, of course...

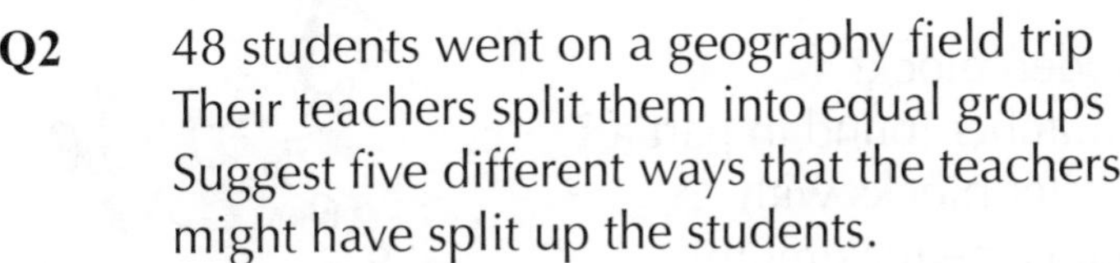

Q2 48 students went on a geography field trip Their teachers split them into equal groups Suggest five different ways that the teachers might have split up the students.

Q3 A school ran 3 evening classes: Conversational French, Cake Making and Woodturning. The Conversational French class had 29 students, Cake Making had 27 students, and the Woodturning class had 23. For which classes did the teacher have difficulty dividing the students into equal groups?

Q4 **a)** Write down the first five cube numbers.
b) Which of the numbers given in part **a)** are multiples of 2?
c) Which of the numbers given in part **a)** are multiples of 3?
d) Which of the numbers given in part **a)** are multiples of 4?
e) Which of the numbers given in part **a)** are multiples of 5?

Q5 Write down the prime factorisation of:
a) 18
b) 140
c) 47

The tricky bit is remembering that a <u>prime factorisation</u> includes <u>all</u> the prime factors that multiply to make that number — so you've got to repeat some of them.

Q6 **a)** List the first five prime numbers.
b) If added together, what is their total?
c) Write down the prime factorisation of the answer to part **b)**.

Q7 **a)** List the first five odd numbers.
b) If added together, what is their total?
c) Write down the prime factorisation of the answer to part **b)**.

Multiples, Factors and Prime Factors

Q8 The prime factorisation of a certain number is $3^2 \times 5 \times 11$.
a) Write down the number.
b) Write down the prime factorisation of 165.

Q9 Gordon is doing some woodwork and needs to calculate the volume of a wooden rectangular block (a cuboid). The length of the block is 50 cm, the height 25 cm and the width 16 cm.
a) What is the volume (in cm³) of the wooden block?
b) What is the prime factorisation of the number found in part a)?
c) Gordon needs to cut the block into smaller blocks with dimensions 4 cm × 5 cm × 5 cm. What is the maximum number of small blocks Gordon can make from the larger block? Make sure you show all your working.

Q10 The prime factorisation of a certain number is $2^3 \times 5 \times 17$.
a) What is the number?
b) What is the prime factorisation of half of this number?
c) What is the prime factorisation of a quarter of the number?
d) What is the prime factorisation of an eighth of the number?

Q11 Bryan and Sue were playing a guessing game. Sue thought of a number between 1 and 100 which Bryan had to guess. Bryan was allowed to ask five questions, which are listed with Sue's responses in the table below.

Bryan's Questions	Sue's Responses
Is it prime?	No
Is it odd?	No
Is it less than 50?	Yes
Is it a multiple of 3?	Yes
Is it a multiple of 7?	Yes

What is the number that Sue thought of?

Start by writing down a number table up to 100. Look at each response in turn and cross off numbers 'till you've only got one left.

LCM and HCF

Millom
Home
Top tip

These two fancy names always put people off — but really they're dead easy. Just learn these simple facts:

1) The Lowest Common Multiple (LCM) is the SMALLEST number that will DIVIDE BY ALL the numbers in question.

E.g. 3, 6, 9, 12, 15 are all multiples of 3.
5, 10, 15, 20, 25 are all multiples of 5.
The lowest number that is in both lists is 15, so 15 is the LCM of 3 and 5.

2) The Highest Common Factor (HCF) is the BIGGEST number that will DIVIDE INTO ALL the numbers in question.

E.g. 1, 2, 4, 8 are all factors of 8.
1, 2, 3, 4, 6, 12 are all factors of 12.
The highest number that is in both lists is 4, so 4 is the HCF of 8 and 12.

Q1 **a)** List the first ten multiples of 6, starting at 6.
b) List the first ten multiples of 5, starting at 5.
c) What is the LCM of 5 and 6?

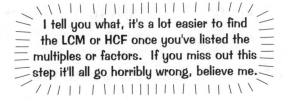

I tell you what, it's a lot easier to find the LCM or HCF once you've listed the multiples or factors. If you miss out this step it'll all go horribly wrong, believe me.

Q2 **a)** List all the factors of 30.
b) List all the factors of 48.
c) What is the HCF of 30 and 48?

Q3 For each set of numbers find the HCF.

a) 40, 60
b) 10, 40, 60
c) 10, 24, 40, 60
d) 15, 45
e) 15, 30, 45
f) 15, 20, 30, 45
g) 32, 64
h) 32, 48, 64
i) 16, 32, 48, 64

Q4 For each set of numbers find the LCM.

a) 40, 60
b) 10, 40, 60
c) 10, 24, 40, 60
d) 15, 45
e) 15, 30, 45
f) 15, 20, 30, 45
g) 32, 64
h) 32, 48, 64
i) 16, 32, 48, 64

Q5 Lars, Rita and Alan regularly go swimming. Lars goes every 2 days, Rita goes every 3 days and Alan goes every 5 days. They all went swimming together on Friday 1st June.

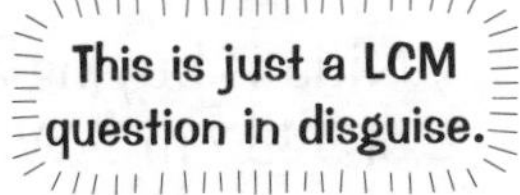
This is just a LCM question in disguise.

a) On what date will Lars and Rita next go swimming together?
b) On what date will Rita and Alan next go swimming together?
c) On what day of the week will all 3 next go swimming together?
d) Which of the 3 (if any) will go swimming on 15th June?

Roots and Reciprocals

Square root just means "WHAT NUMBER TIMES ITSELF (i.e. 2×2) GIVES..."
The square roots of 64 are 8 and –8 because 8×8=64 and -8×-8=64.
Cube root means "WHAT NUMBER TIMES ITSELF TWICE (i.e. 2×2×2) GIVES ..."
The cube root of 27 is 3 because 3×3×3=27.
Square roots always have a + and – answer, cube roots only have 1 answer.

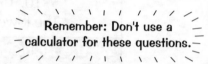

Remember: Don't use a calculator for these questions.

Q1 Write down the reciprocals of the following values. Leave your answers as whole numbers or fractions.

a) 7 **b)** 12 **c)** $\frac{3}{8}$ **d)** $-\frac{1}{2}$

Q2 Work out the reciprocals of the following values. Write your answers as whole numbers or fractions.

a) 20 **b)** $\sqrt{16}$ **c)** 0.5 **d)** 1.5

Q3 Write down both answers to each of the following:

a) $\sqrt{4}$ = ... **d)** $\sqrt{49}$ = ... **g)** $\sqrt{144}$ = ...
b) $\sqrt{16}$ = ... **e)** $\sqrt{25}$ = ... **h)** $\sqrt{64}$ = ...
c) $\sqrt{9}$ = ... **f)** $\sqrt{100}$ = ... **i)** $\sqrt{81}$ = ...

Q4 Find the value of the following:

a) $\sqrt[3]{64}$ = ...
b) $\sqrt[3]{1000}$ = ...
c) $\sqrt[3]{125}$ = ...
d) $\sqrt[3]{216}$ = ...

Q5 Nida is buying a small storage box online. She sees a cube box with volume of 343 cm^3. What is the length of each box edge?

Q6 A farmer is buying fencing to surround a square field of area 3600 m^2. What length of fencing does he need to buy?

Powers

Hang on there. Before you try this page, make sure you know all the rules for dealing with powers...

The small number is called the <u>power</u> or <u>index number.</u> Remember the plural of index is <u>indices.</u>

$5^4 = 5 \times 5 \times 5 \times 5 =$ ____
we say "five to the power four"

$8^3 = 8 \times 8 \times 8 =$ ____
we say "eight to the power three" or "eight cubed"

Q1 Complete the following:

a) $2^4 = 2 \times 2 \times 2 \times 2 \quad =$
b) $10^3 = 10 \times 10 \times 10 \quad =$
c) $3^5 = 3 \times \ldots \quad =$
d) $4^6 = 4 \times \ldots \quad =$
e) $1^9 = 1 \times \ldots \quad =$
f) $5^6 = 5 \times \ldots \quad =$

Q2 Simplify the following:

a) $2 \times 2 \times 2 \times 2 \times 2 \times 2 \times 2 \times 2$
b) $12 \times 12 \times 12 \times 12 \times 12$
c) $x \times x \times x \times x \times x$
d) $m \times m \times m$
e) $y \times y \times y \times y$
f) $z \times z \times z \times z \times z \times z$

Q3 Which of the following are <u>true</u>?

a) $2^4 \times 2^6 = 2^{10}$
b) $2^2 \times 2^3 \times 2^4 = 2^9$
c) $2^3 \times 2^2 = 2^6$
d) $4^{10} \times 4^4 \times 4^2 = 4^{18}$
e) $2^1 \times 2^3 \times 2^4 = 2^8$
f) $10^4 \times 10^2 = 10^8$
g) $2^{20} \div 2^5 = 2^4$
h) $3^{12} \div 3^4 = 3^8$
i) $4^6 \div 6^4 = 4^2$
j) $10^{20} \div 10^3 = 10^{17}$
k) $4^6 \div (4^2 \times 4^3) = 4^1$
l) $9^2 \times (9^{30} \div 9^{25}) = 9^{10}$

Q4 Remove the brackets from the following and express as a single power:

a) $(3^4 \times 3^2) \div (3^6 \times 3^3)$
b) $(4^{10} \times 4^{12}) \times 4^3$
c) $10^2 \div (10^3 \times 10^{12})$
d) $(3^6)^{-2}$
e) $4^2 \times 4^{-1} \times 4^6 \times (4^2 \div 4^3)$
f) $(5^2 \times 5^3) \div (5^6 \div 5^4)$

Q5 Work out the following:

a) $144^{\frac{1}{2}} =$
b) $20^1 \times 20^0 =$
c) $\dfrac{81^{\frac{1}{2}} \times 9^2}{9^3} =$

Standard Index Form

Writing very big (or very small) numbers gets a bit messy with all those zeros if you don't use this standard index form. But of course, the main reason for knowing about standard form is... you guessed it — it's in the Exam.

Q1 Delilah is doing some calculations for her science homework. She needs to give her answers as ordinary numbers. How should she write the following answers?

a) 3.56×10
b) 3.56×10^3
c) 3.56×10^{-1}
d) 3.56×10^4
e) 0.082×10^2
f) 0.082×10^{-2}
g) 0.082×10
h) 0.082×10^{-1}
i) 157×10
j) 157×10^{-3}
k) 157×10^3
l) 157×10^{-1}

Q2 Write in standard form:

a) 2.56
b) 25.6
c) 0.256
d) 25 600
e) 95.2
f) 0.0952
g) 95 200
h) 0.000952
i) 4200
j) 0.0042
k) 42
l) 420.

Q3 Write in standard form:

a) 34.7×10
b) 73.004
c) 0.005×10^3
d) 9183×10^2
e) 15 million
f) 937.1×10^4
g) 0.000075
h) 0.05×10^{-2}
i) 534×10^{-2}
j) 621.03
k) 149×10^2
l) 0.003×10^{-4}.

When scientists write about massive things such as the universe, or tiny things such as cells and particles, it's often more convenient to write numbers in standard form. Write the numbers in Questions 4 to 7 in standard form.

Q4 The average diameter of a cell nucleus in a mammal is around 0.006 mm.

Q5 A billion = a thousand million   A trillion = a thousand billion.

Q6 A light year is 9 460 000 000 000 km (approx).

Q7 Nautilus covered 69 138 miles before having to refuel.

Q8 A tissue sample is three cells thick. Each cell has a thickness of 0.000004 m. What is the thickness of the tissue sample, in mm? Give your answer in standard form.

Q9 This table gives the diameter and distance from the Sun of some planets.

Planet	Distance from Sun (km)	Diameter (km)
Earth	1.5×10^8	1.3×10^4
Venus	1.085×10^8	1.2×10^4
Mars	2.28×10^8	6.8×10^3
Mercury	5.81×10^7	4.9×10^3
Jupiter	7.8×10^8	1.4×10^5
Neptune	4.52×10^9	4.9×10^4
Saturn	1.43×10^9	1.2×10^5

From the table write down which planet is:

a) smallest in diameter
b) largest in diameter
c) nearest to the Sun
d) furthest from the Sun.

Write down which planets are:

e) nearer to the Sun than the Earth
f) bigger in diameter than the Earth.

Fractions

Answer the following questions without using a calculator.

Q1 Carry out the following multiplications, giving your answers in their lowest terms:

a) $\frac{1}{8} \times \frac{1}{8}$ **c)** $\frac{3}{18} \times \frac{1}{3}$ **e)** $1\frac{1}{4} \times 4\frac{1}{8}$

b) $\frac{2}{3} \times \frac{1}{6}$ **d)** $1\frac{1}{4} \times 3\frac{1}{8}$ **f)** $\frac{9}{10} \times \frac{9}{100} \times \frac{1}{100}$

Q2 Carry out the following divisions, giving your answers in their lowest terms:

a) $\frac{1}{8} \div \frac{1}{8}$ **c)** $\frac{3}{18} \div \frac{1}{3}$ **e)** $1\frac{1}{4} \div 4\frac{1}{8}$

b) $\frac{2}{3} \div \frac{1}{6}$ **d)** $1\frac{1}{4} \div 3\frac{1}{8}$ **f)** $\left(\frac{9}{10} \div \frac{9}{100}\right) \div \frac{1}{100}$

Q3 Evaluate the following, giving your answers in their lowest terms:

a) $\frac{1}{8} + \frac{1}{8}$ **c)** $\frac{3}{18} + \frac{1}{3}$ **e)** $1\frac{1}{4} + 4\frac{1}{8}$

b) $\frac{1}{6} + \frac{2}{3}$ **d)** $1\frac{1}{4} + 3\frac{1}{8}$ **f)** $\frac{9}{10} + \frac{9}{100} + \frac{1}{100}$

Q4 Caley is making some punch for her birthday party. She mixes $\frac{1}{2}$ litre of cranberry juice, $1\frac{1}{2}$ litres of apple juice, $\frac{2}{3}$ litre of orange juice and $\frac{4}{5}$ litres of pineapple juice. She has a bowl that will hold 4 litres. Will this be big enough to contain all of the punch?

Q5 Evaluate the following, giving your answers in their lowest terms:

a) $\frac{1}{8} - \frac{1}{8}$ **c)** $\frac{3}{18} - \frac{1}{3}$ **e)** $1\frac{1}{4} - 4\frac{1}{8}$

b) $\frac{2}{3} - \frac{1}{6}$ **d)** $3\frac{1}{8} - 1\frac{1}{4}$ **f)** $\left(\frac{9}{10} - \frac{9}{100}\right) - \frac{1}{100}$

Q6 Evaluate the following, giving your answers in their lowest terms:

a) $\frac{1}{2} + \frac{1}{4}$ **e)** $6 \times \frac{2}{3}$ **i)** $3 + \frac{8}{5}$

b) $\frac{2}{3} - \frac{1}{4}$ **f)** $\frac{4}{5} \div \frac{2}{3}$ **j)** $\frac{2}{3}\left(\frac{3}{4} + \frac{4}{5}\right)$

c) $\frac{1}{5} + \frac{2}{3} - \frac{2}{5}$ **g)** $\frac{5}{12} \times \frac{3}{2}$ **k)** $\left(\frac{1}{7} + \frac{3}{14}\right) \times \left(3 - \frac{1}{5}\right)$

d) $5 - \frac{1}{4}$ **h)** $\frac{5}{6} - \frac{7}{8}$ **l)** $\left(\frac{3}{4} - \frac{1}{5}\right) \div \left(\frac{7}{8} + \frac{1}{16}\right)$

Saturday

Fractions, Decimals and Percentages

I reckon that converting decimals to percentages is about as easy as it gets — so make the most of it.

Q1 Express each of the following as a percentage:

a) 0.25
b) 0.5
c) 0.75
d) 0.1
e) 0.4152
f) 0.8406
g) 0.3962
h) 0.2828

All you're doing is multiplying by 100 — it really couldn't be easier.

Q2 Express each percentage as a decimal:

a) 50%
b) 12%
c) 40%
d) 34%
e) 60.2%
f) 54.9%
g) 43.1%
h) 78.8%

Now you're dividing by 100 — so just move the decimal point to the left.

Q3 Express each of the following as a percentage:

a) $\frac{1}{2}$
b) $\frac{1}{4}$
c) $\frac{1}{8}$
d) $\frac{3}{4}$
e) $\frac{1}{25}$
f) $\frac{2}{3}$

Q4 Express each percentage as a fraction in its lowest terms:

a) 25%
b) 60%
c) 45%
d) 30%
e) 8.2%
f) 49.6%
g) 88.6%
h) 32.4%

Best thing to do with e)-h) is to put them over 100, then get rid of the decimal point by multiplying top and bottom by 10. Then just cancel down as normal.

Q5 200 out of 250 houses on an estate have DVD players. What percentage is this?

Q6 In an exam Tina scored 52/80. The grade she receives depends on the percentage scored. What grade will Tina get?

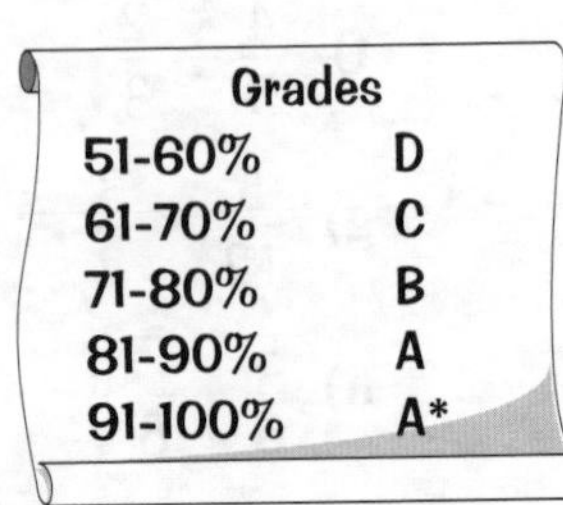

Grades	
51-60%	D
61-70%	C
71-80%	B
81-90%	A
91-100%	A*

Fractions and Decimals

Decimals are just another way of writing fractions — so it's easy to convert between the two...

Q1 Write the following fractions as decimals:

a) $\frac{3}{10}$ **b)** $\frac{37}{100}$ **c)** $\frac{2}{5}$ **d)** $\frac{3}{8}$

e) $\frac{14}{8}$ **f)** $\frac{8}{64}$ **g)** $\frac{24}{40}$ **h)** $\frac{4}{80}$

Q2 Fill in the gaps in the following conversion table :

Fraction	Decimal
½	0.5
⅕	
	0.125
	1.6
4⁄16	
7⁄2	
	0.x
x⁄100	
3⁄20	
	0.45

Q3 Write the following decimals as fractions in their lowest form:

a) 0.6 **b)** 0.75 **c)** 0.95 **d)** 0.128

e) $0.\dot{3}$ **f)** $0.\dot{6}$ **g)** $0.\dot{1}$

Q4 Write the following recurring decimals as fractions:

a) 0.222... **b)** 0.444... **c)** 0.888... **d)** 0.808080...

e) 0.121212... **f)** 0.545545545... **g)** 0.753753753... **h)** 0.156156156...

Manipulating Surds and Rational Numbers

Well, to be honest, I think the idea of rational and irrational numbers is a bit odd. Basically, a rational number is either a whole number or one you can write as a fraction. An irrational number... you guessed it... is not whole and can't be written as a fraction.

Q1 Write down a value of x for which $x^{1/2}$ is:

a) irrational
b) rational

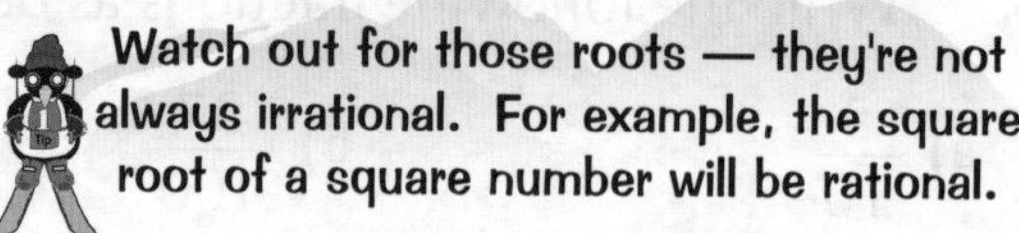

Watch out for those roots — they're not always irrational. For example, the square root of a square number will be rational.

Q2 Which of the following powers of $\sqrt{3}$ are rational and which are irrational?

a) $(\sqrt{3})^1$ **c)** $(\sqrt{3})^3$

b) $(\sqrt{3})^2$ **d)** $(\sqrt{3})^4$

Q3 Four of the following numbers are rational and two are irrational:
$\sqrt{2}\times\sqrt{8}$, $(\sqrt{5})^6$, 6π, 0.4, $49^{-1/2}$, $\sqrt{6}+6$

a) Write down the four rational numbers.
b) Write down the two irrational numbers.

Q4 Which of the following are rational and which are irrational?

a) $16^{1/2}$ **b)** $16^{1/3}$ **c)** $2^{1/2}$

Q5 Simplify:

Remember — $\sqrt{a}\times\sqrt{b}=\sqrt{(ab)}$.

a) $\sqrt{5}\times\sqrt{3}$ **b)** $\dfrac{\sqrt{20}}{\sqrt{5}}$ **c)** $\sqrt{4}-\sqrt{1}$ **d)** $\left(\dfrac{\sqrt{5}}{\sqrt{2}}\right)^2$

e) $(\sqrt{x})^2$ **f)** $\sqrt{x^2}$ **g)** $\sqrt{8}\times\sqrt{8}$ **h)** $\sqrt{18}-\sqrt{9}$

Q6 Give an example of two different irrational numbers, x and y, where x/y is a rational number.

Q7 **a)** Write down a rational number which is greater than 1 but less than 2.
b) Write down an irrational number which lies between 1 and 2.
c) If P is a non-zero rational number, is $1/P$ also a rational number? Clearly show your reasoning.

Don't forget that recurring decimals, like 0.333333333, can be put into fraction form, like $\frac{1}{3}$ — so they're rational too.

X and Y Coordinates

Q1 ABCD is a parallelogram. A is (-1, 3), B is (-2,-1) and C is (4,-1).
Draw axes with x from -3 to 5 and y from -2 to 4.
Plot A, B and C then find the missing coordinates for D.

Q2 Draw axes with x from -9 to 9 and y from -12 to 12.
On the same set of axes draw the following shapes and find their missing pair of coordinates.

a) ABCD is a square
A is (1, 1)
B is ?
C is (-3,-3)
D is (-3, 1)

b) ABCD is a parallelogram
A is (2, 8)
B is (6, 8)
C is ?
D is (1, 5)

c) ABCD is a rectangle
A is ?
B is (3,-8)
C is (3,-6)
D is (-5,-6)

d) ABCD is a kite
A is (-9, 3)
B is (-6, 8)
C is (-4, 8)
D is ?

e) ABCD is a parallelogram
A is (-2,-10)
B is (4,-10)
C is (6,-12)
D is ?

f) ABCD is a parallelogram
A is (-8, 10)
B is (-6, 10)
C is ?
D is (-5, 12)

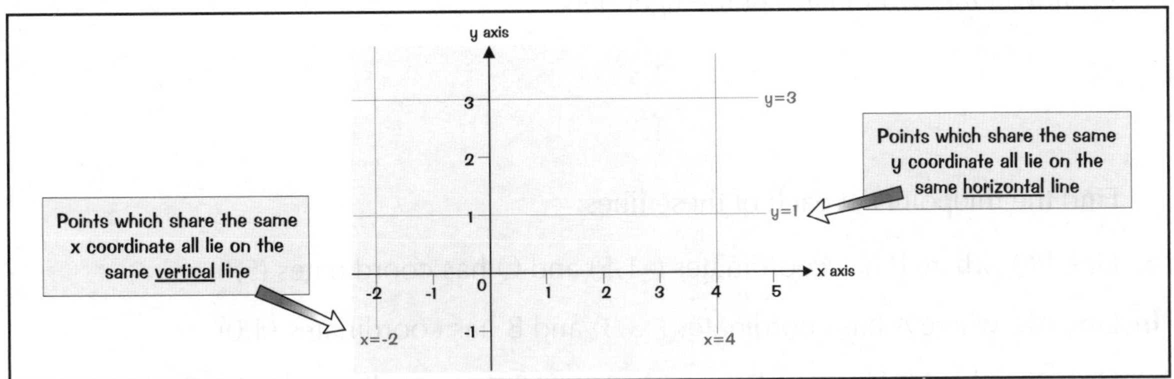

Q3 ABCD is a rectangle with the line $x = 0$ as a line of symmetry.
Draw axes with x from -3 to 3 and y from -3 to 3.
If A = (-2,-2) and B is (-2, 1), find the coordinates of C and D.

I'm afraid you'll just have to get the hang of using things like "the line x = 4", as they seem to prefer it to "a vertical line through the point 4 on the horizontal axis". Yeah, that is a bit long winded, I guess — so maybe they've got a point...

X and Y Coordinates

Q4 Find the midpoint of the line AB, where A and B have coordinates:

a) A(2,3) B(4,5)

b) A(1,8) B(10,2)

c) A(0,11) B(11,11)

d) A(3,15) B(14,3)

e) A(6,7) B(0,0)

f) A(16,16) B(3,3)

g) A(8,33) B(32,50)

h) A(17,28) B(44,13)

ahh... nice'n'easy...

Your answers should be coordinates too.

Q5 Anna is designing the plan of a kitchen using some computer aided design software. The coordinates of the room on screen are (0, 10), (220, 10), (0, 260), (220, 260). She needs to enter the coordinates of the ceiling light, which will be exactly in the centre of the room. What will the coordinates of the light be?

Q6 Find the midpoints of each of these lines:

a) Line PQ, where P has coordinates (–1,5) and Q has coordinates (5,6).

b) Line AB, where A has coordinates (–3,3) and B has coordinates (4,0).

c) Line RS, where R has coordinates (4,–5) and S has coordinates (0,0).

d) Line PQ, where P has coordinates (–1,–3) and Q has coordinates (3,1).

e) Line GH, where G has coordinates (10,13) and H has coordinates (–6,–7).

f) Line CD, where C has coordinates (–4,6) and D has coordinates (12,–7).

g) Line MN, where M has coordinates (–5,–8) and N has coordinates (–21,–17).

h) Line AB, where A has coordinates (–1,0) and B has coordinates (–9,–14).

Straight Line Graphs

Q1 Which letters represent the following lines:

a) $x = y$
b) $x = 5$
c) $y = -x$
d) $x = 0$
e) $y = -7$
f) $x + y = 0$
g) $y = 5$
h) $x - y = 0$
i) $y = 0$
j) $x = -7$?

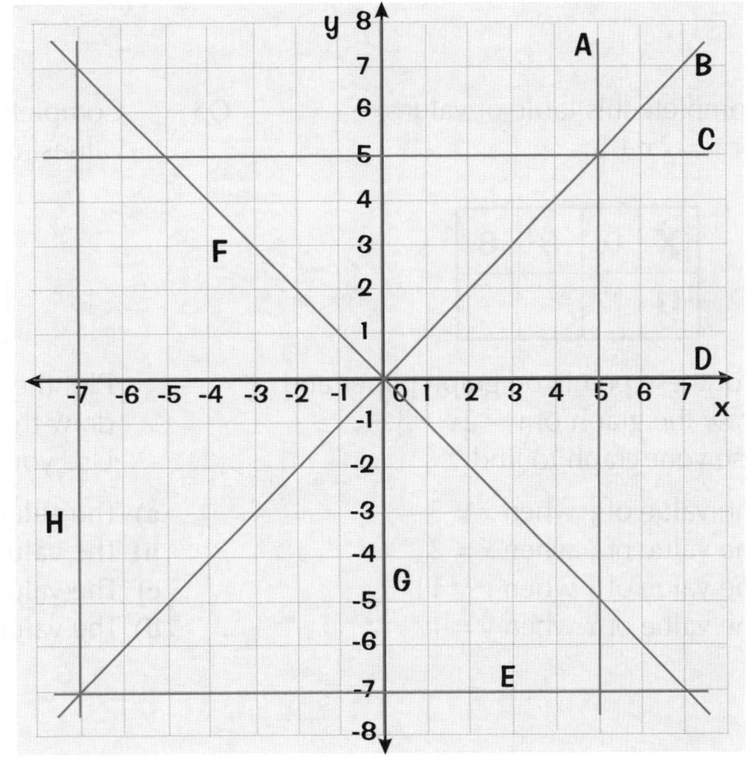

Don't get confused if you've got "x + y = ... " — just rearrange the equation to "y = -x + ..." and as if by magic, you've got a line you recognise.

Q2 Complete the following table for the line $y = 3x - 1$:

x	-4	-3	-2	-1	0	1	2	3	4
3x									
-1									
y									

Plot these points on graph paper and hence draw the graph of $y = 3x - 1$.
Use a scale of 1 cm for 2 units on the y-axis and 2 cm for 1 unit on the x-axis.

Q3 Complete the following table for the line $y = \frac{1}{2}x - 3$:

x	-6	-4	-2	0	2	4	6
½ x							
-3							
y							

Plot these points on graph paper and hence draw the graph of $y = \frac{1}{2}x - 3$.

Straight Line Graphs

If you know it's a straight line, you only really need <u>two</u> points, but it's always a <u>good idea</u> to plot three — it's a bit of a safety net, really.

Q4 Complete this table of values for $y = 2x + 3$:

x	0	3	8
y			

Plot these points on graph paper and draw the graph of $y = 2x + 3$.
Use your graph to find:

a) The value of y when $x = 5$
b) The value of y when $x = 2$
c) The value of x when $y = 11$
d) The value of x when $y = 17$

Q5 Complete this table of values for $y = \frac{1}{4}x - 3$:

x	-8	-4	8
y			

Plot these points on graph paper and draw the graph of $y = \frac{1}{4}x - 3$.
Use your graph to find:

a) The value of y when $x = 2$
b) The value of y when $x = 0$
c) The value of x when $y = -2$
d) The value of x when $y = -1.5$

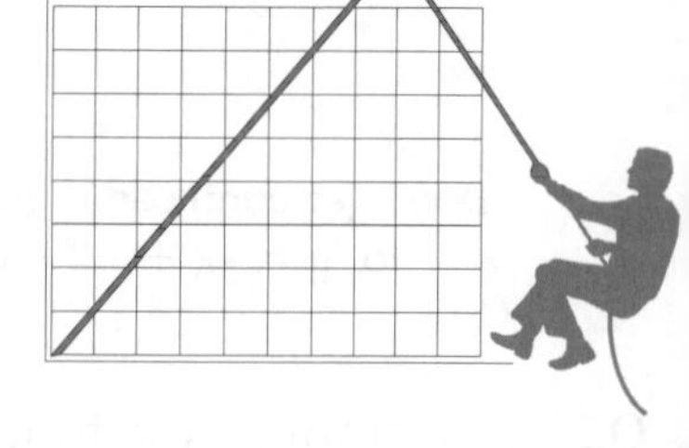

Q6 The cost of electricity is calculated using the formula:
Total cost = Fixed charge + (cost per unit × number of units).
Customers can choose two different methods of payment:

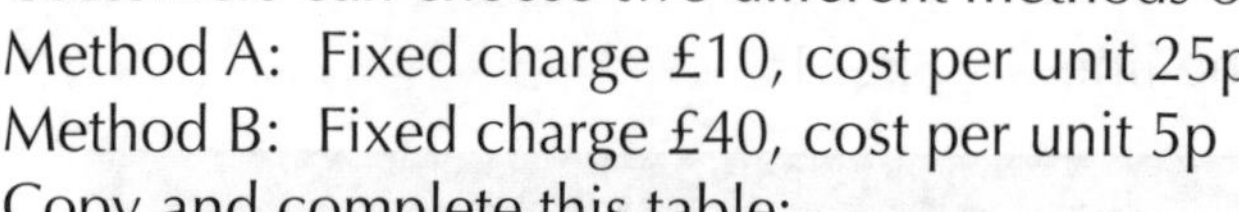

Method A: Fixed charge £10, cost per unit 25p
Method B: Fixed charge £40, cost per unit 5p
Copy and complete this table:

Number of Units used	0	100	200	300
Cost using method A				
Cost using method B				

Plot these points on a graph (put the number of units on the horizontal axis, cost on the vertical axis):

a) Use your graph to find the total cost when 70 units are used for:
  i) Method A
  ii) Method B

b) Miss Wright used 75 units. Which method should she use to minimize her bill, Method A or Method B?

c) Use your graph to work out how many units Miss Wright would have to use for both methods to cost the same amount.

y = mx + c

Writing the equation of a line in the form y = mx + c gives you a nifty way of finding the gradient and y-intercept. Remember that — it'll save you loads of time. Anything for an easy life...

Q1 For each of the following lines, give the gradient and the coordinates of the point where the line cuts the *y*-axis.

a) $y = 4x + 3$
b) $y = 3x - 2$
c) $y = 2x + 1$
d) $y = -3x + 3$
e) $y = 5x$
f) $y = -2x + 3$
g) $y = -6x - 4$
h) $y = x$
i) $y = -\frac{1}{2}x + 3$
j) $y = \frac{1}{4}x + 2$
k) $3y = 4x + 6$
l) $2y = -5x - 4$
m) $8y = 4x - 12$
n) $3y = 7x + 5$
o) $x + y = 0$
p) $x - y = 0$
q) $y - x = 3$
r) $x - 3 = y$
s) $y - 7 = 3x$
t) $y - 5x = 3$
u) $y + 2x + 3 = 0$
v) $y - 2x - 4 = 0$

I know these are a bit algebra-ish, but don't worry, they won't bite.

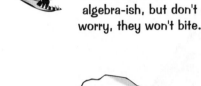

Q2 What is the gradient of:

a) line A
b) line B
c) line C
d) line D
e) line E
f) line F
g) line G
h) line H
i) line I
j) line J
k) a line parallel to A
l) a line parallel to B

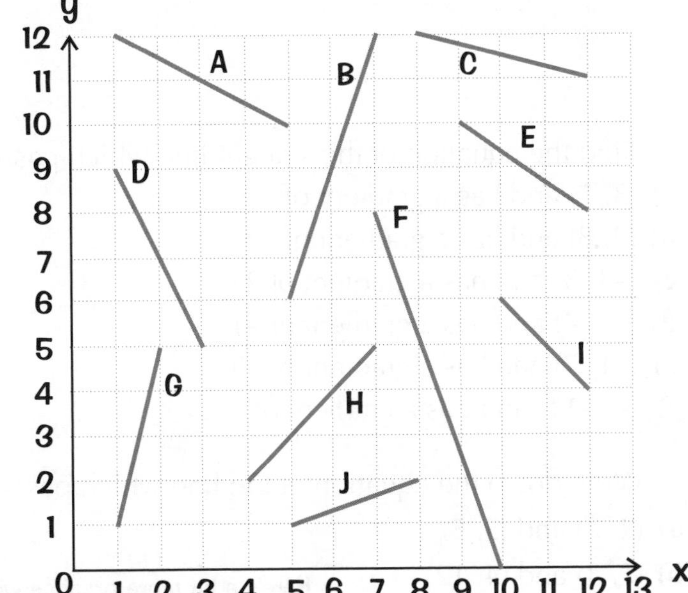

Uphill gradients are always positive, downhill always negative. Impressed? Hmmm....thought not. Can be a bit of an uphill battle, these.

Q3 What is the gradient of the lines joining the points:

a) (3, 5) and (5, 9)
b) (6, 3) and (10, 5)
c) (-6, 4) and (-3, 1)
d) (8, 2) and (4, 10)
e) (8, 5) and (6, 4)
f) (-3, -1) and (1, -4)?

Q4 Lauren works in a ski resort grading ski runs. A blue run has a gradient shallower than -0.2, a red is steeper than a blue, but has a gradient shallower than -0.25. Anything steeper is a black.
A run covers a horizontal distance of 1.75 km long and descends 400 meters.
What colour should Lauren grade it?

$y = mx + c$

Q5 Find the equations of the following lines:

a) A
b) B
c) C
d) D
e) E
f) F

Yeah, OK, this sounds a bit scary, but just work out the gradient (m) and look at the y-intercept (c) and pop them back into "y = mx + c"... easy lemons.

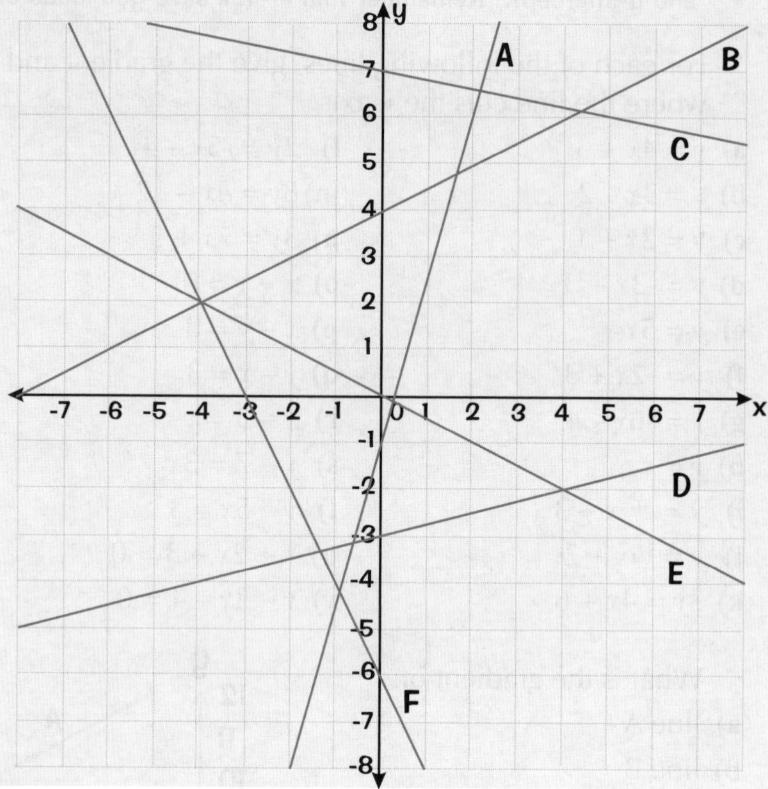

Q6 Find the equation of the straight line which passes through:

a) (3, 7) and has a gradient of 1
b) (2, 8) and has a gradient of 3
c) (–3, 3) and has a gradient of 2
d) (4, –4) and has a gradient of –1
e) (–1, 7) and has a gradient of –3
f) (4, –11) and has a gradient of –2.

Q7 Write down the equation of the line which passes through the points:

a) (2, 2) and (5, 5)
b) (1, 3) and (4, 12)
c) (–2, –3) and (5, 11)
d) (1, 0) and (5, –12)
e) (–5, 6) and (–1, –2)
f) (4, 23) and (–2, –7).

Here's a bit more practice with those gradients. Thought you'd like that.

Q8 What is the value of x or y if:

a) the point $(x, 13)$ is on the line $y = 3x + 1$
b) the point $(x, -2)$ is on the line $y = \frac{1}{2}x - 6$
c) the point $(4, y)$ is on the line $y = 2x - 1$
d) the point $(-3, y)$ is on the line $y = -3x$?

Q9 Which of the following points lie on the line $y = 3x - 1$?
(7, 20), (6, 15), (5, 14)

Equations From Graphs

Q1 Two variables x and y are connected by the equation $y = mx + c$. Use the table to draw a graph with x on the horizontal axis and y on the vertical axis.

x	1	3	5	8
y	9	17	25	37

Use your graph to find the value of:

a) m

b) c

— and hence:

c) write down the equation connecting x and y.

d) Use your equation to find the value of y when:

i) $x = 6$

ii) $x = 10$

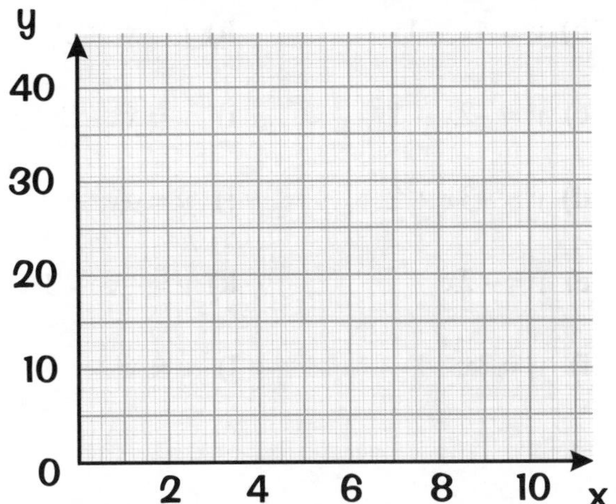

Q2 Two variables x and y are connected by the equation $y = ax + b$.

Here are some values of x and y.

x	4	9	16	25
y	5	7.5	11	15.5

Use the table to draw a graph. Plot x on the horizontal axis using a scale of 1 cm to 2 units and y on the vertical using a scale of 1 cm to 1 unit.

Use your graph to find:

a) the value of a

b) the value of b.

c) Write down the equation connecting x and y.

Q3 CGPtronics semiconductor company plans to release a new microprocessor. It costs a certain amount to design, and a certain amount per unit to manufacture. The table below shows the total production cost for producing different numbers of microprocessors.

Units	10 000	30 000	50 000	70 000
Production cost	£23 000	£29 000	£35 000	£41 000

a) Plot the data from the table on a graph.

b) Use the graph to work out the cost of designing the microprocessor. Use this amount to work out the manufacturing cost per unit.

c) Write down an equation connecting the number of units made to the production cost.

d) CGPtronics want to sell the microprocessors for 80p each. On the same set of axes, plot a graph showing the revenue from selling different numbers of microprocessors.

revenue = value of sales

e) How many microprocessors will CGPtronics have to sell to break even?

Graphs to Recognise

Q1 Here are some equations, and there are some curves below. Match the equations to the curves on this page and the following page.

a) $y = 3x + 1$

b) $y = 4x - 1$

c) $y = -2x - 1$

d) $y = -3x + 2$

e) $y = -2x$

f) $y = 3x$

g) $y = -x^2$

h) $y = x^2 + 2$

i) $y = x^2 - 3$

j) $y = -x^2 + 3$

k) $y = -x^2 - 3$

l) $y = x^2$

m) $y = x^3 + 3$

n) $y = 2x^3 - 3$

o) $y = -\frac{1}{2}x^3 + 2$

p) $y = -x^3 + 3$

q) $y = x^3$

r) $y = -\frac{3}{x}$

s) $y = \frac{2}{x}$

t) $y = \frac{1}{x^2}$

u) $y = -\frac{1}{x^2}$

i)

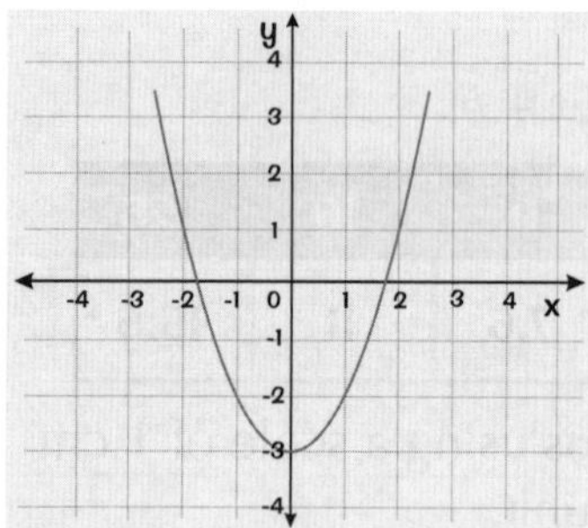

ii)

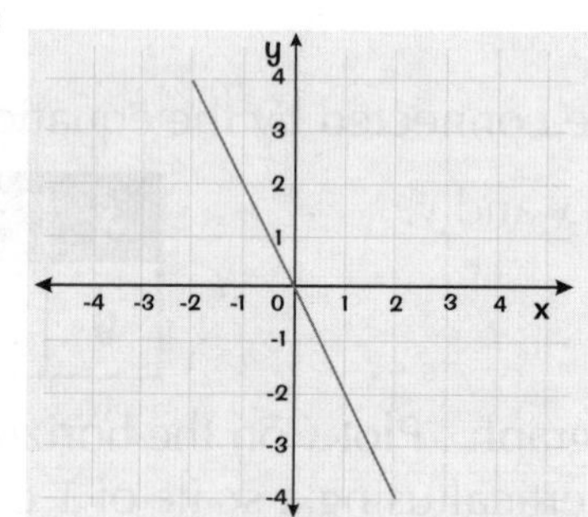

iii)

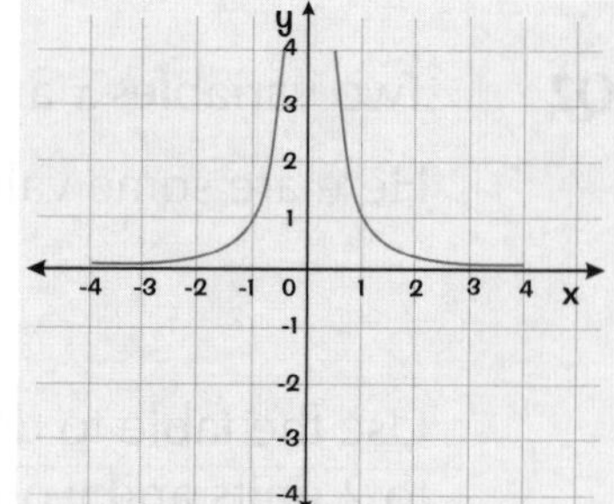

iv)

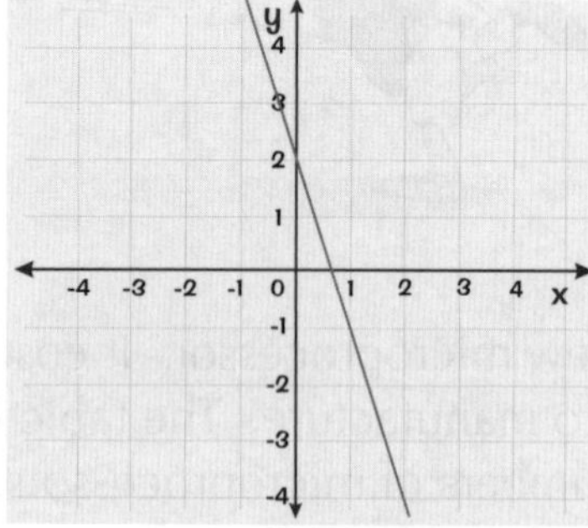

v)

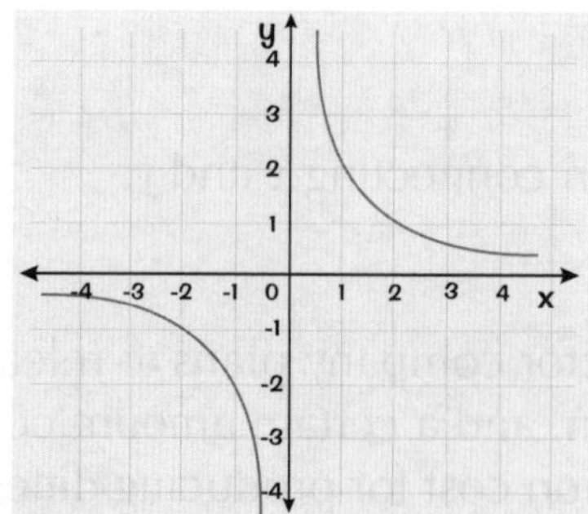

vi)

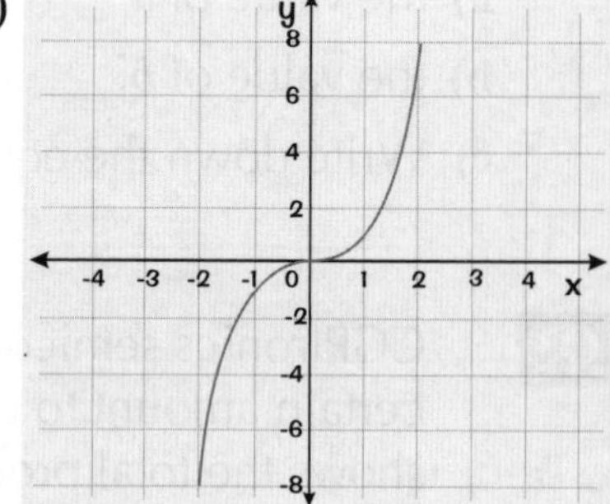

vii)

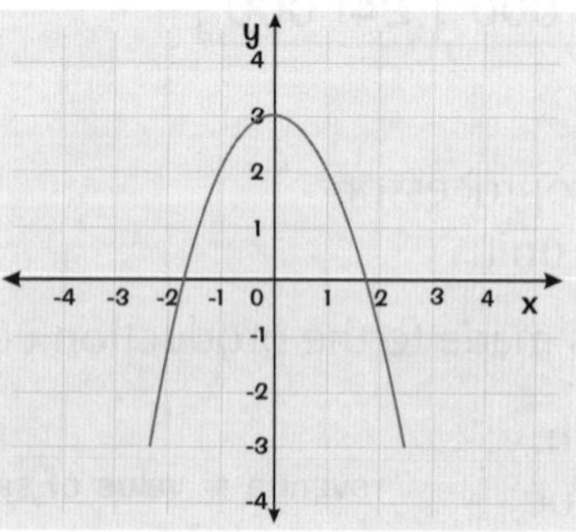

viii)

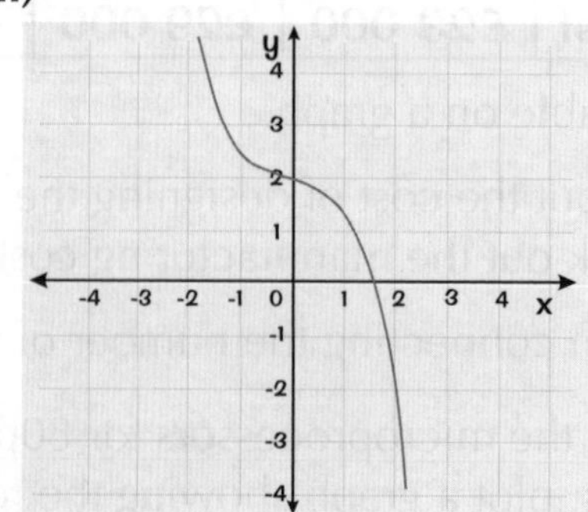

ix)

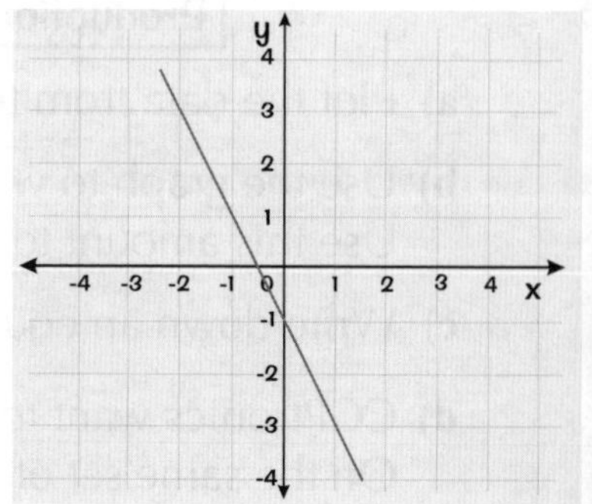

Graphs to Recognise

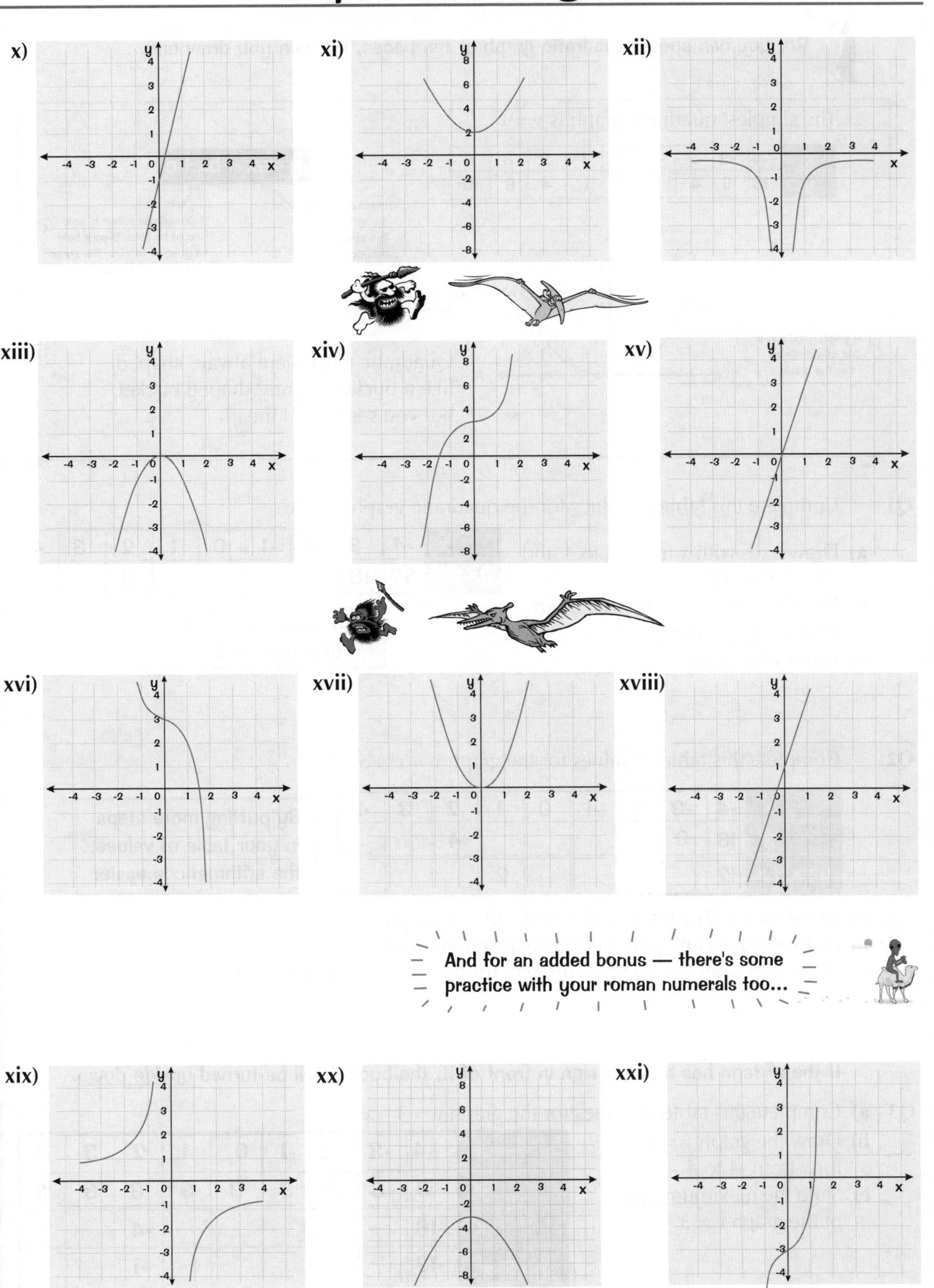

Quadratic Graphs

So, you can spot a quadratic graph at ten paces, but can you draw one...

The simplest quadratic graph is $y = x^2$

x	-4	-3	-2	-1	0	1	2	3	4
y	16	9	4	1	0	1	4	9	16

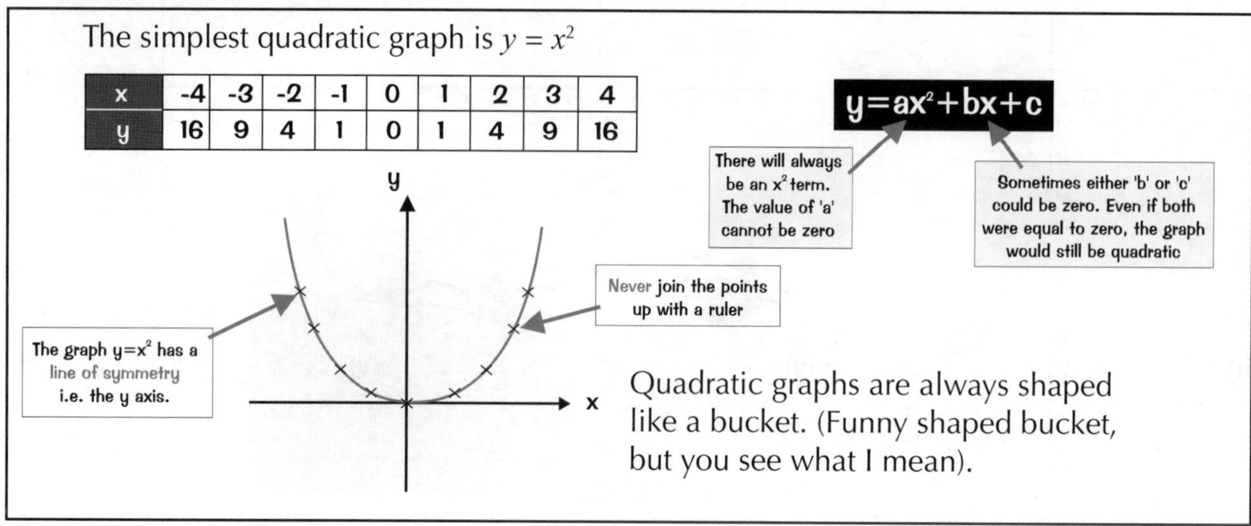
y=ax²+bx+c
There will always be an x² term. The value of 'a' cannot be zero
Sometimes either 'b' or 'c' could be zero. Even if both were equal to zero, the graph would still be quadratic
y
x
Never join the points up with a ruler
The graph y=x² has a line of symmetry i.e. the y axis.

Quadratic graphs are always shaped like a bucket. (Funny shaped bucket, but you see what I mean).

Q1 Complete this <u>table of values</u> for the quadratic graph $y = 2x^2$.

x	-4	-3	-2	-1	0	1	2	3	4
$y=2x^2$	32	18					8		

Remember to square first then × 2

a) Draw axes with x from -4 to 4 and y from 0 to 32.
b) Plot these 9 points and join them with a <u>smooth curve</u>.
c) Label your graph.

Q2 Complete this table of values for the graph $y = x^2 + x$.

x	-4	-3	-2	-1	0	1	2	3	4
x^2	16	9					4		
$y=x^2+x$	12					2			

By putting more steps in your table of values, the arithmetic is easier

a) Draw axes with x from -4 to 4 and y from 0 to 20.
b) Plot the points and join them with a smooth curve.
c) Draw and label the <u>line of symmetry</u> for the quadratic graph $y = x^2 + x$.

If the x^2 term has a <u>minus</u> sign in front of it, the bucket will be turned <u>upside down</u>.

Q3 **a)** Complete this table of values for the graph $y = 3 - x^2$.
b) Draw the graph $y = 3 - x^2$ for x from -4 to 4.
c) State the <u>maximum value</u> of the graph $y = 3 - x^2$.

x	-4	-3	-2	-1	0	1	2	3	4
3	3	3	3	3	3	3	3	3	3
$-x^2$	-16						-4		
$y=3-x^2$	-13						-1		

Sunday 15th

Cubic Graphs

You go about a cubic in the same way as you would a quadratic — but you should get a different shaped graph, of course. It's always a good idea to put lots of steps in the table of values — that way it's easier to check any points that look wrong.

Q1 Complete this table of values for $y = x^3$:

x	-3	-2	-1	0	1	2	3
$y=x^3$							

Draw the graph of $y = x^3$.

Q2 Complete this table of values for $y = -x^3$:

x	-3	-2	-1	0	1	2	3
$y=-x^3$							

Draw the graph of $y = -x^3$.

Q3 Complete this table of values for $y = x^3 + 4$:

x	-3	-2	-1	0	1	2	3
x^3							
+4							
y							

Draw the graph of $y = x^3 + 4$.

Remember — no rulers.

Q4 Complete this table of values for $y = -x^3 - 4$:

x	-3	-2	-1	0	1	2	3
$-x^3$							
-4							
y							

Draw the graph of $y = -x^3 - 4$.

Q5 Look at your graphs for questions 1 and 3. What has been done to graph 1 to change it into graph 3? Without plotting a table of values draw the graph of $y = x^3 - 4$.

Q6 Look at your graphs for questions 2 and 4. What has been done to graph 2 to change it into graph 4? Without plotting a table of values draw the graph of $y = -x^3 + 4$.

Graphs: Shifts and Stretches

You've got to learn the rules for these shifts and stretches — there are only 4 types, so it won't take long. If you don't, either you'll have to spend ages working it out, or worse still you'll have to guess. Seems a bit of a waste of time and marks to me...

Q1 This is a graph of $y = f(x)$.

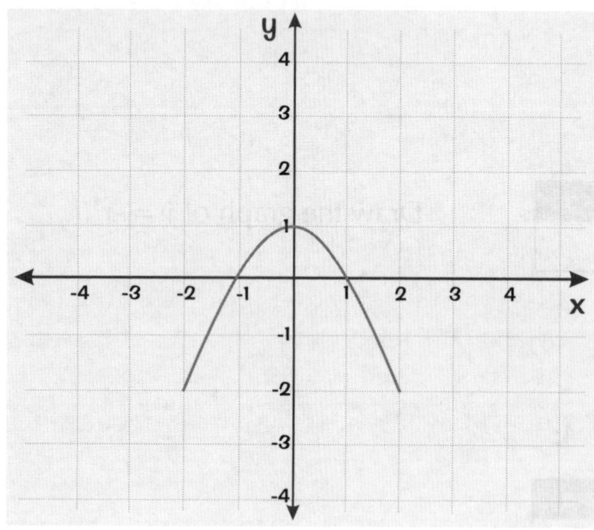

Use the graph of $y = f(x)$ to sketch:

a) $y = f(x) + 3$
b) $y = f(x) - 3$
c) $y = f(x + 3)$
d) $y = f(x - 3)$
e) $y = -f(x)$
f) $y = f(2x)$
g) $y = f(\frac{1}{2}x)$
h) $y = -f(2x)$

Q2 This is a graph of $y = f(x)$.

Use the graph of $y = f(x)$ to sketch:

a) $y = f(x) + 2$
b) $y = f(x) - 2$
c) $y = f(x + 2)$
d) $y = f(x - 2)$
e) $y = -f(x)$
f) $y = f(2x)$
g) $y = f(\frac{1}{2}x)$
h) $y = f(x + 3) - 1$
i) $y = f(x - 1) + 3$

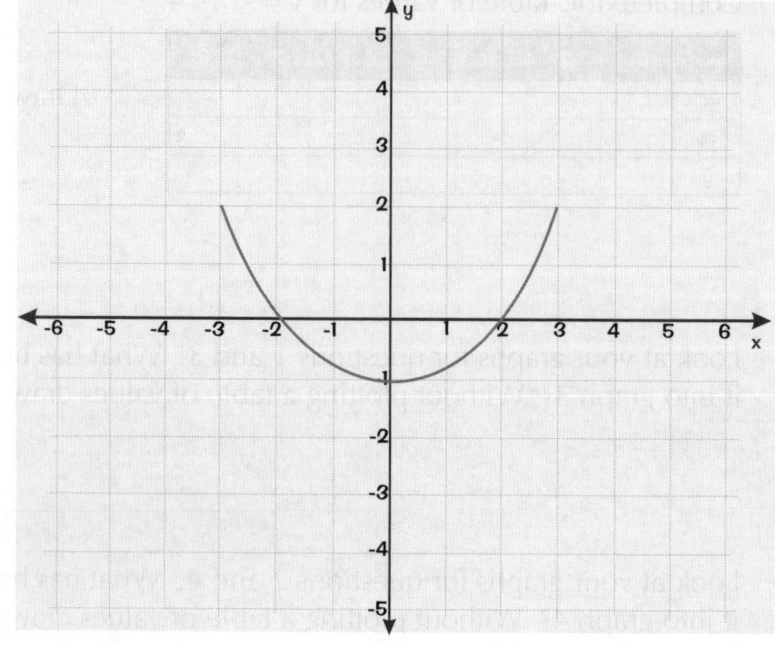

Graphs: Shifts and Stretches

Q3 A sound engineer wants to alter a recorded sound.
The sound wave has the equation $y = \sin(x)$, as shown below.

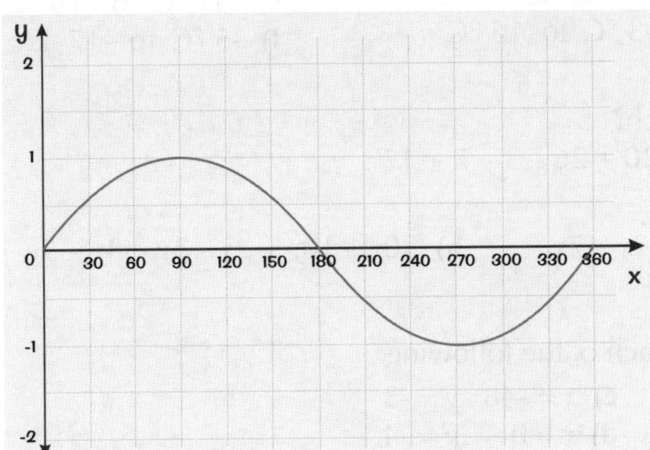

Draw what the engineer will see on the monitor if the altered sound wave has the equation:

a) $y = 2\sin(x)$

b) $y = \sin(2x)$.

Q4 This is the graph of $y = \cos(x)$:

Draw the graphs of:

a) $y = 2\cos(x)$

b) $y = \cos(2x)$.

Q5 This is the graph of $y = f(x)$:
Sketch the graphs of:

a) $y = f(x) + 1$

b) $y = -f(x)$

c) $y = f(x + 1)$

d) $y = f(\frac{1}{2}x)$

e) $y = f(2x)$

f) $y = 2f(x)$

g) $y = f(x + 1) - 2$.

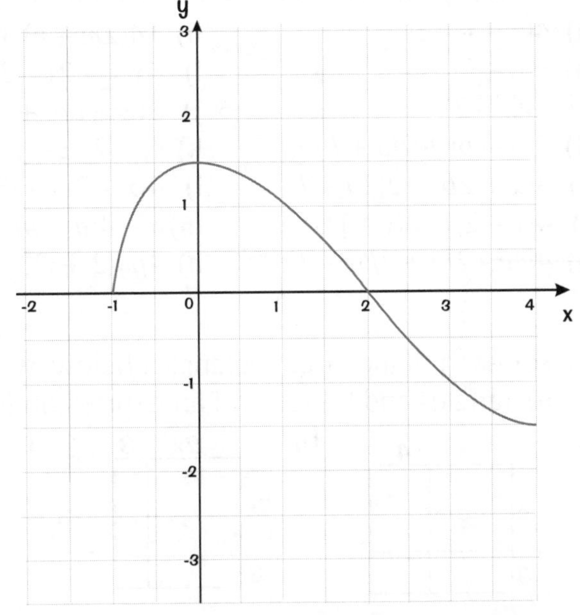

Algebra

Q1 Work out the following temperature changes:

a) 20 °C to -7 °C
b) -10 °C to -32 °C
c) -17 °C to -5 °C
d) -3 °C to 15 °C
e) -31 °C to -16 °C
f) -5 °C to -17 °C

Q2 Which is larger and by how much?

a) -12 + 7 – 4 + 6 – 2 + 7 or **b)** -30 + 26 – 3 – 7 + 17

Q3 Simplify: **a)** $4x - 5x + 3x - x + 2x - 7x$ **b)** $30y - 10y + 2y - 3y + 4y - 5y$

Q4 Find the value of xy and $\frac{x}{y}$ for each of the following:

a) $x = -100$ $y = 10$
b) $x = 24$ $y = -4$
c) $x = -48$ $y = -3$
d) $x = 0$ $y = -4$

Q5 Find the value of $(a - b) \div (c + d)$ when $a = 10$, $b = -26$, $c = -5$ and $d = -4$.

Q6 Simplify the following:

a) $2x \times -3y$
b) $-8a \times 2b$
c) $-4x \times -2x$
d) $4p \times -4p$
e) $-30x \div -3y$
f) $50x \div -5y$
g) $10x \div -2y$
h) $-30x \div -10x$
i) $40ab \div -10ab$
j) $70x^2 \div -7x^2$
k) $-36x^2 \div -9x$
l) $40y^2 \div -5y$

Q7 Simplify the following by collecting like terms together:

a) $3x^2 + 4x + 12x^2 - 5x$
b) $14x^2 - 10x - x^2 + 5x$
c) $12 - 4x^2 + 10x - 3x^2 + 2x$
d) $20abc + 12ab + 10bac + 4b$
e) $8pq + 7p + q + 10qp - q + p$
f) $15ab - 10a + b - 7a + 2ba$
g) $4pq - 14p - 8q + p - q + 8p$
h) $13x^2 + 4x^2 - 5y^2 + y^2 - x^2$
i) $11ab + 2cd - ba - 13dc + abc$
j) $3x^2 + 4xy + 2y^2 - z^2 + 2xy - y^2 - 5x^2$

Q8 Multiply out the brackets and simplify where possible:

a) $4(x + y - z)$
b) $x(x + 5)$
c) $-3(x - 2)$
d) $7(a + b) + 2(a + b)$
e) $3(a + 2b) - 2(2a + b)$
f) $4(x - 2) - 2(x - 1)$
g) $4e(e + 2f) + 2f(e - f)$
h) $14(2m - n) + 2(3n - 6m)$
i) $4x(x + 2) - 2x(3 - x)$
j) $3(2 + ab) + 5(1 - ab)$
k) $(x - 2y)z - 2x(x + z)$
l) $4(x - 2y) - (5 + x - 2y)$
m) $a - 4(a + b)$
n) $4pq(2 + r) + 5qr(2p + 7)$
o) $x^2(x + 1)$
p) $4x^2\left(x + 2 + \frac{1}{x}\right)$
q) $8ab(a + 3 + b)$
r) $7pq\left(p + q - \frac{1}{p}\right)$
s) $4[(x + y) - 3(y - x)]$

Q9 For each of the large rectangles below, write down the area of each of the small rectangles and hence find an expression for the area of each large rectangle.

a)

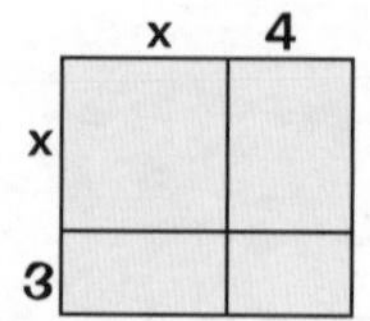

b)

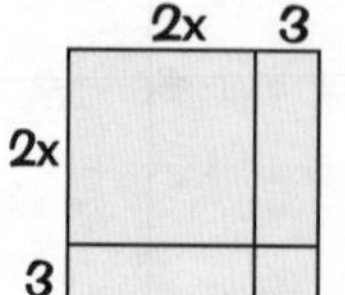

c)

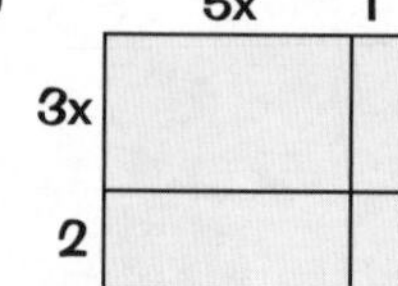

Eeeek — loads of questions...

Algebra

Q10 Multiply out the brackets and simplify your answers where possible:

a) $(x-3)(x+1)$
b) $(x-3)(x+5)$
c) $(x+10)(x+3)$
d) $(x-5)(x-2)$
e) $(x+2)(x-7)$
f) $(4-x)(7-x)$
g) $(2+3x)(3x-1)$
h) $(3x+2)(2x-4)$
i) $(x-3)(4x+1)$
j) $2(2x+y)(x-2y)$
k) $4(x+2y)(3x-2y)$
l) $(3x+2y)^2$

Q11 Find the product of $5x-2$ and $3x+2$.

Q12 Find the square of $2x-1$.

Q13 A rectangular pond has length $(3x-2)$ m and width $(5-x)$ m.
Write down a simplified expression for:

a) the pond's perimeter
b) the pond's area.

Q14 A rectangular bar of chocolate consists of 20 small rectangular pieces. The size of a small rectangular piece of chocolate is 2 cm by x cm.

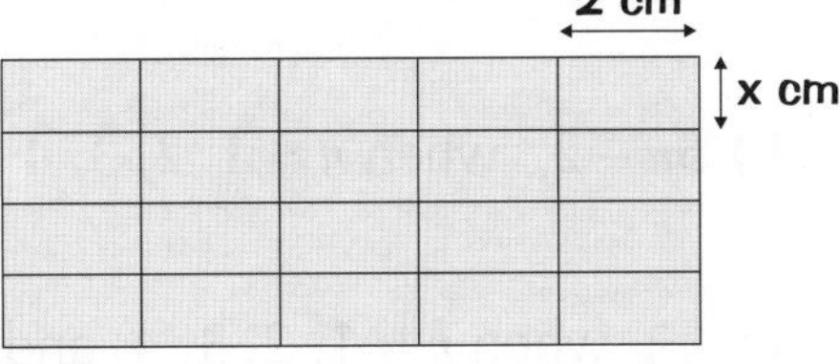

a) Write down an expression for the perimeter of the whole bar.
b) Write down an expression for the area of the whole bar.
c) If I ate 6 small rectangular pieces of chocolate, what is the area of the remaining bar?

Q15 Find a simplified expression for the perimeter *and* the area of the following shapes.

a)

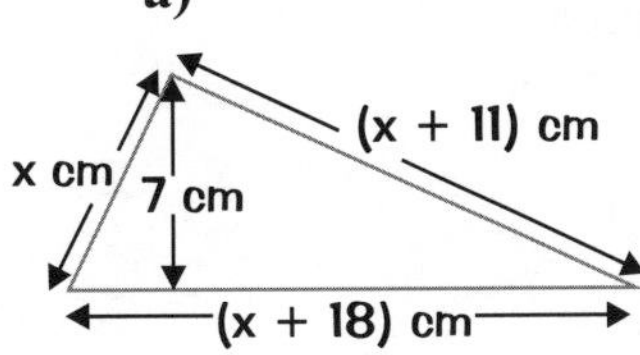

b)

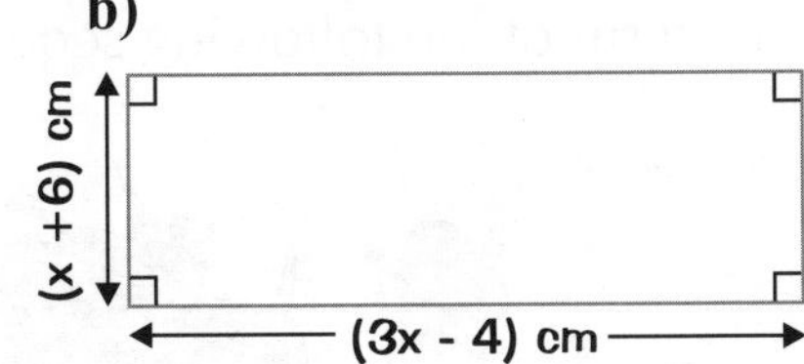

c)

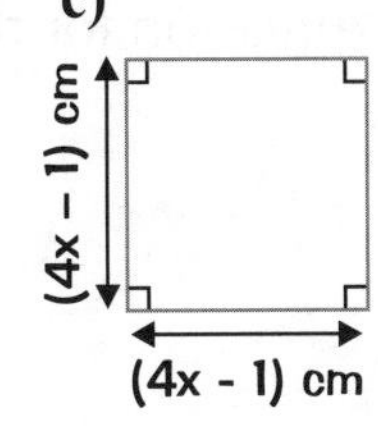

d)

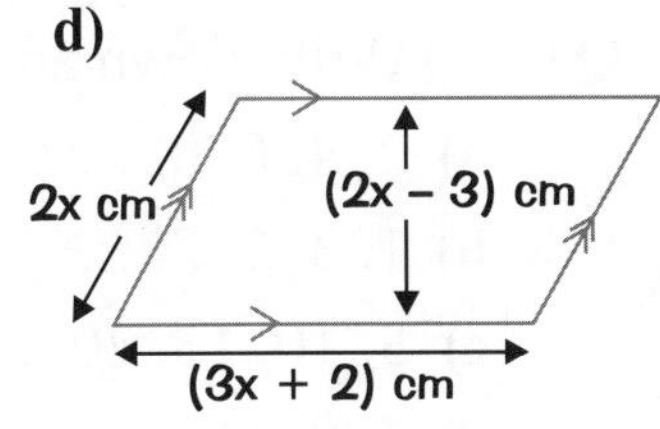

Q16 All the expressions below have a^2 as a common factor. Factorise each of them.

a) $a^2b + a^2c$
b) $5a^2 + 13a^2b$
c) $2a^2b + 3a^2c$
d) $a^3 + a^2y$
e) $2a^2x + 3a^2y + 4a^2z$
f) $a^2b^2 + a^3c^2$

Q17 Factorise and simplify the following:

a) $4xyz + 8xyz$ **b)** $8xyz + 12xyz$ **c)** $8xyz + 16x^2yz$ **d)** $20x^2y^2z^2 + 16xyz^2$

Sequences

Q1 For each of the sequences below, write down the next three numbers and the rule that you used.

a) 1, 3, 5, 7,...

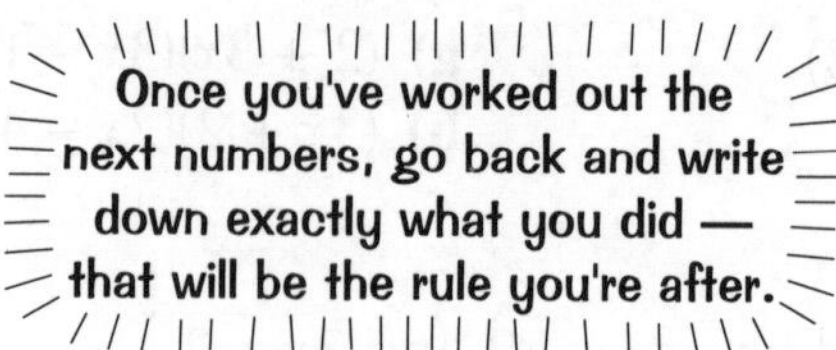

Once you've worked out the next numbers, go back and write down exactly what you did — that will be the rule you're after.

b) 2, 4, 8, 16,...

c) 3, 30, 300, 3000,...

d) 3, 7, 11, 15,...

e) 19, 14, 9, 4, –1,...

Q2 For the following, use the rule given to generate the first 5 terms of the sequence.

a) $3n + 1$, when $n = 1, 2, 3, 4$ and 5.

b) $5n - 2$, when $n = 1, 2, 3, 4$ and 5.

c) n^2, when $n = 1, 2, 3, 4$, and 5.

d) $n^2 - 3$, when $n = 1, 2, 3, 4$, and 5.

Q3 Write down an expression for the nth term of the following sequences:

a) 2, 4, 6, 8, ...
b) 1, 3, 5, 7, ...
c) 5, 10, 15, 20, ...
d) 5, 8, 11, 14, ...

Q4 In the following sequences, write down the next 3 terms and the nth term:

a) 7, 10, 13, 16,...
b) 12, 17, 22, 27,...
c) 6, 16, 26, 36,...
d) 54, 61, 68, 75,...

Sequences

10, 20, 15, 17½, 16¼...

a) Write down the next 4 terms.

b) Explain how you would work out the 10th term.

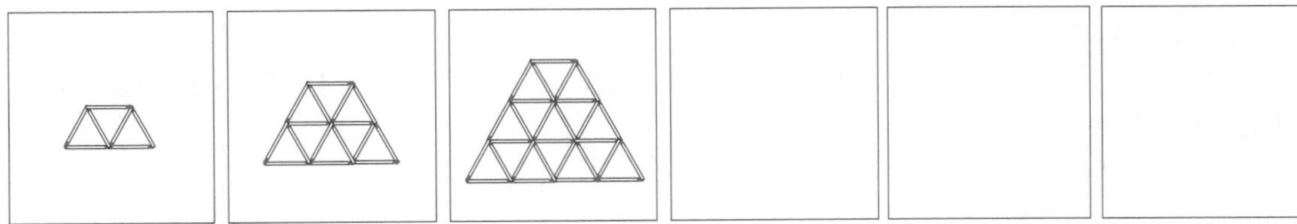

The pattern above is based on individual triangles.

a) Write down the number of individual triangles in each group shown above.

b) Work out the number of individual triangles that would be in each of the next three groups.

c) Find a formula for the number of individual triangles in the nth term of the pattern.

For the increasing/decreasing difference type questions you've got to work out how much the difference changes by each time.

Write down the next three terms and nth term of:

a) 5, 8, 12, 17,...

b) 6, 9, 14, 21,...

c) 9, 12, 19, 30,...

d) 14, 19, 27, 38,...

Q8

Hannah is tiling her kitchen floor. She's making a square pattern with grey and white tiles. In the centre there will be a grey tile. The rest of the pattern will be made up of alternating grey and white tiles, with the four corner tiles of the square being grey.
Assume that $n = 1$ in the pattern shown opposite.

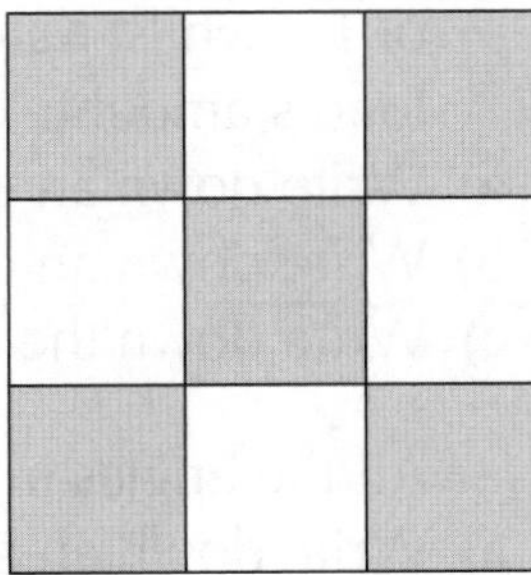

Work out, in terms of n, the formula for:

a) the number of grey tiles Hannah will need to buy

b) the number of white tiles she will need to buy

c) the total number of tiles needed.

Solving Equations

Q1 When 1 is added to a number and the answer then trebled, it gives the same result as doubling the number and then adding 4. Find the number.

Q2 Solve the following:

a) $3x + 1 = 2x + 6$
b) $4x + 3 = 3x + 7$
c) $5x - 1 = 3x + 19$
d) $x + 2 = \frac{1}{2}x - 1$
e) $x + 15 = 4x$
f) $3x + 3 = 2x + 12$

Q3 Solve the following:

a) $3x - 8 = 7$
b) $2(x - 3) = -2$
c) $4(2x - 1) = 60$
d) $2x - 9 = 25$
e) $\frac{24}{x} + 2 = 6$
f) $5x - 2 = 6x - 7$

Q4

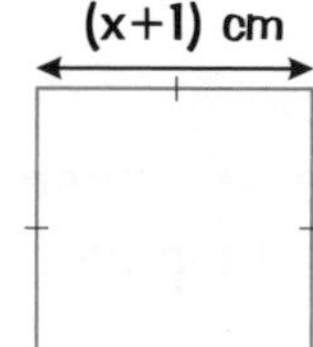

A square has sides of length $(x + 1)$ cm. Find the value of x if:

a) the perimeter of the square is 66 cm
b) the perimeter of the square is 152.8 cm.

With these wordy ones, you just have to write your own equation from the information you're given.

Q5 Mr Smith sent his car to the local garage. He spent £x on new parts, four times this amount on labour and finally £29 for an MOT test. If the total bill was for £106.50, find the value of x.

Q6 Solve:

a) $2(x - 3) - (x - 2) = 5$
b) $5(x + 2) - 3(x - 5) = 29$
c) $2(x + 2) + 3(x + 4) = 31$
d) $10(x + 3) - 4(x - 2) = 7(x + 5)$
e) $5(4x + 3) = 4(7x - 5) + 3(9 - 2x)$
f) $3(7 + 2x) + 2(1 - x) = 19$
g) $\frac{x}{3} + 7 = 12$
h) $\frac{x}{10} + 18 = 29$
i) $\frac{120}{x} = 16$
j) $41 - \frac{x}{11} = 35$
k) $\frac{x}{100} - 3 = 4$

Q7 Joan, Kate and Linda win £2400 on the Lottery between them. Joan gets a share of £x, whilst Kate gets twice as much as Joan. Linda's share is £232 less than Joan's amount.

a) Write down an expression for the amounts Joan, Kate and Linda win.
b) Write down an equation in terms of x, and solve it.
c) Write down the amounts Kate and Linda receive.

Q8 All the angles in the diagram are right angles.

a) Write down an expression for the perimeter of the shape.
b) Write down an expression for the area of the shape.
c) For what value of x will the perimeter and area be numerically equal?

Big blobs and broomsticks...

Solving Equations

Q9 Solve the following:

a) $5(x-1)+3(x-4)=-11$

b) $3(x+2)+2(x-4)=x-3(x+3)$

c) $\frac{3x}{2}+3=x$

d) $3(4x+2)=2(2x-1)$

e) $\frac{5x+7}{9}=3$

f) $\frac{2x+7}{11}=3$

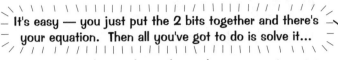

It's easy — you just put the 2 bits together and there's your equation. Then all you've got to do is solve it...

Q10 For what value of x is the expression $14-\frac{x}{2}$ equal to the value $\frac{3x-4}{2}$?

Q11 Two men are decorating a room. One has painted 20 m^2 and the other only 6 m^2. They continue painting and manage to paint another x m^2 each. If the first man has painted exactly three times the area painted by the second man, find the value of x.

Q12 Carol's father was 24 years old when Carol was born. Now he is four times as old as Carol. How old is Carol?

Q13 Mr Jones is 4 years older than his wife and 31 years older than his son. Their ages add up to 82 years. If Mr Jones is x years old, find the value of x and find the ages of his wife and son.

Q14 Solve the following:

a) $\frac{y}{2}+2=13$

b) $\frac{3x}{4}-2=4$

c) $\frac{3}{5}(4x-3)=15$

d) $\frac{1}{5}(x-4)=3$

e) $\frac{2}{3}(x+1)=16$

f) $\frac{2z}{5}-3=-5$

Q15 A train travels at 70 mph for x hours and then at 80 mph for $3\frac{3}{4}$ hours. If the train covers 405 miles of track, find the value of x.

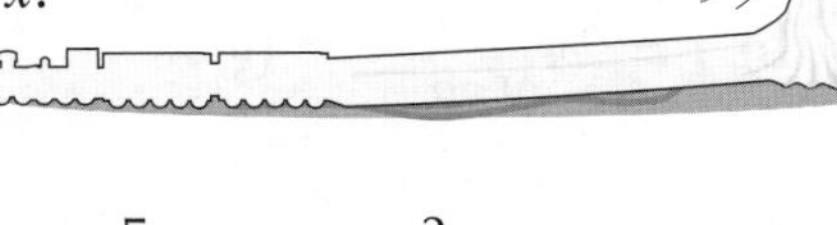

Q16 Solve the following:

a) $\frac{4x+3}{2}+x=\frac{5x+41}{4}$

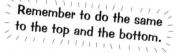

Remember to do the same to the top and the bottom.

b) $\frac{5}{7}(x-2)-\frac{3}{4}(x+3)=-4$

Q17 A triangle has lengths as shown below. Find the length of each side, if the length of AC exceeds that of AB by ½ cm.

A
(6x - 4) cm
(3x + 1) cm
B
C
5x cm

Rearranging Formulas

Rearranging is getting the letter you want out of the formula and making it the subject. And it's exactly the same method as for solving equations, which can't be bad.

Q1 Rearrange the following formulas to make the letter in brackets the new subject.

a) $g = 10 - 4h$ (h)

b) $d = \frac{1}{2}(c + 4)$ (c)

c) $j = -2(3 - k)$ (k)

d) $a = \frac{2b}{3}$ (b)

e) $f = \frac{3g}{8}$ (g)

f) $y = \frac{x}{2} - 3$ (x)

g) $s = \frac{t}{6} + 10$ (t)

Q2 Jason is saving up to go travelling next year and has got a temporary job selling cars. He is paid a basic wage of £500 a month, plus a bonus of £50 for each car he sells. He has a spreadsheet to keep track of his money, which calculates his wages (£w) after working for m months and selling c cars, using the following formula:

$$w = 500m + 50c$$

a) Rearrange the formula to make c the subject.

b) Find the number of cars Jason needs to sell in 11 months to earn £12 100.

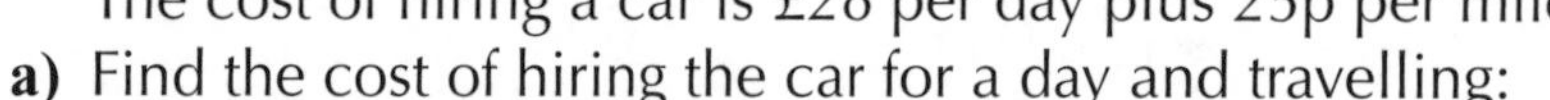

Q3 The cost of hiring a car is £28 per day plus 25p per mile.

a) Find the cost of hiring the car for a day and travelling:

i) 40 miles

ii) 80 miles

b) Write down a formula to give the cost of hiring a car (£c) for one day, and travelling n miles.

c) Rearrange the formula to make n the subject.

d) How many miles can you travel, during one day, if you have a budget of:

i) £34, **ii)** £50, **iii)** £56.50.

Q4 Rearrange the following formulas to make the letter in brackets the new subject.

a) $y = \sqrt{(x + 3)}$ (x)

b) $t = 2\pi\sqrt{\frac{l}{g}}$ (g)

c) $f = \frac{10 + g}{3}$ (g)

d) $w = \frac{5 - z}{2}$ (z)

Q5 Mrs Smith buys x jumpers for £J each and sells them in her shop for a total price of £T.

a) Write down an expression for the amount of money she paid for all the jumpers.

b) Using your answer to **a)**, write down a formula for the profit £P Mrs Smith makes selling all the jumpers.

c) Rearrange the formula to make J the subject.

d) Given that Mrs Smith makes a profit of £156 by selling 13 jumpers for a total of £364 find the price she paid for each jumper originally.

Rearranging Formulas

Q6 A website offering digital photo printing charges 12p per print plus 60p postage.

a) Find the cost of ordering:
i) 12 prints.
ii) 24 prints.

b) Write down a formula for the cost C, in pence, of ordering x prints.

c) Rearrange the formula to make x the subject.

d) A regular customer is looking through old receipts to check she has been charged the right amount. How many prints should she have received in each of her last three transactions if she was charged:
i) £4.92
ii) £6.36
iii) £12.12.

Q7 Rearrange the following formulas, by collecting terms in x and looking for common factors, to make x the new subject.

a) $xy = z - 2x$
b) $ax = 3x + b$
c) $4x - y = xz$
d) $xy = 3z - 5x + y$
e) $xy = xz - 2$
f) $2(x - y) = z(x + 3)$
g) $xyz = x - y - wz$
h) $3y(x + z) = y(2z - x)$

Q8 Rearrange the following to make the letter in brackets the new subject.

a) $pq = 3p + 4r - 2q$ (p)
b) $fg + 2e = 5 - 2g$ (g)
c) $a(b - 2) = c(b + 3)$ (b)
d) $4(a - b) + c(a - 2) = ad$ (a)
e) $2\sqrt{x} + y = z\sqrt{x} + 4$ (x)
f) $\frac{a}{b} = \frac{1}{3}(b - a)$ (a)
g) $\frac{m + n}{m - n} = \frac{3}{4}$ (m)
h) $\sqrt{\frac{(d - e)}{e}} = 7$ (e)
i) $\frac{x - 2y}{xy} = 3$ (y)

These are getting quite tricky — you've got to collect like terms, before you can make anything else the subject.

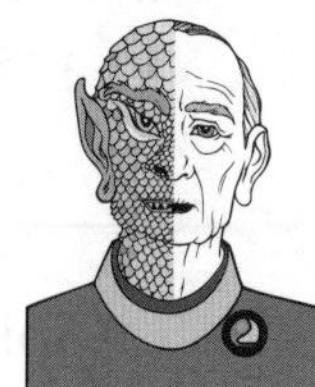

Q9 Rearrange the following formulas to make y the new subject.

a) $x(y - 1) = y$

b) $x(y + 2) = y - 3$

Inequalities

Yet another one of those bits of Maths that looks worse than it is — these are just like equations, really, except for the symbols.

Q1 Write down the inequality represented by each diagram below.

a)
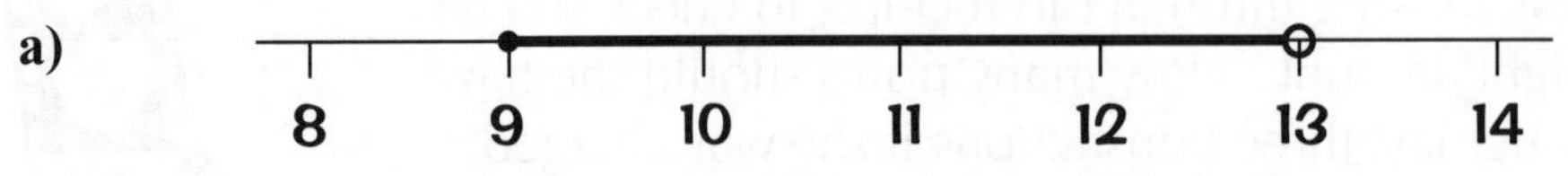

b)
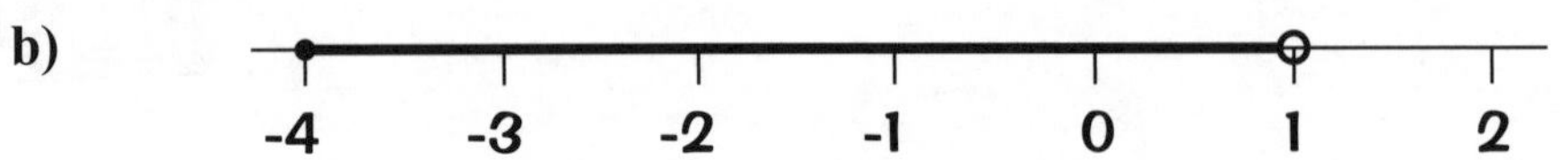

c)
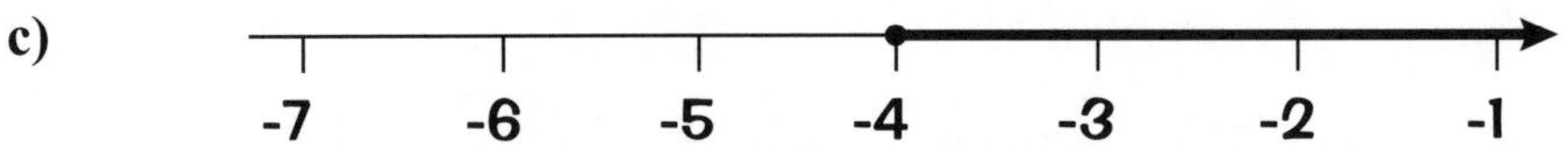

d)
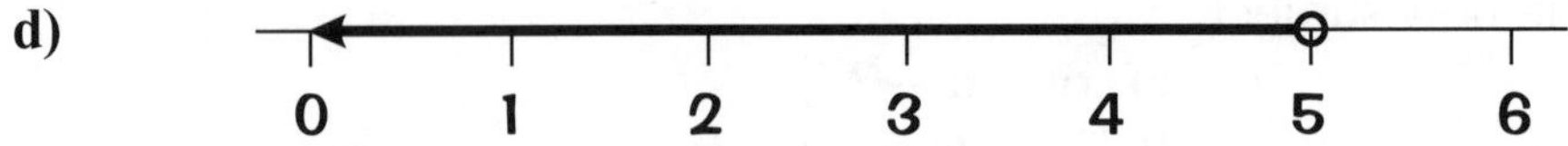

e)
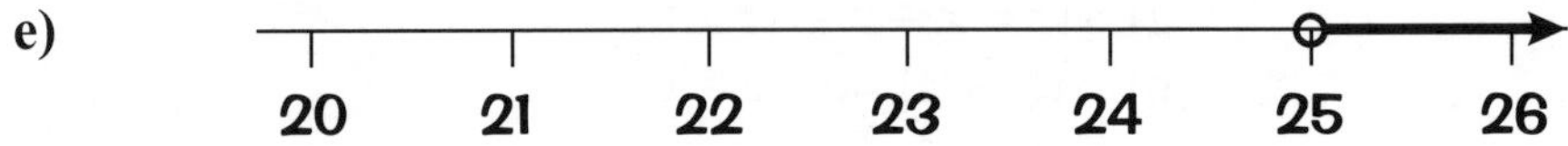

f)
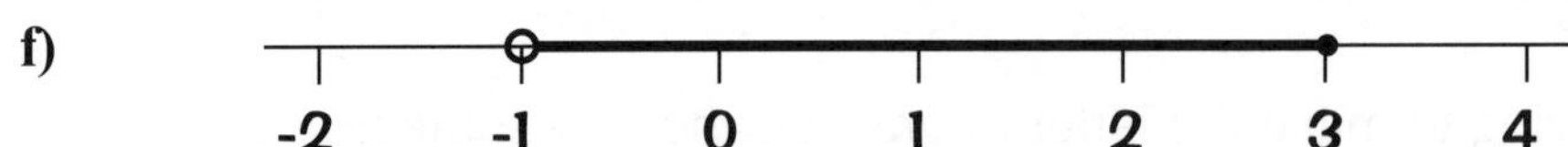

g)
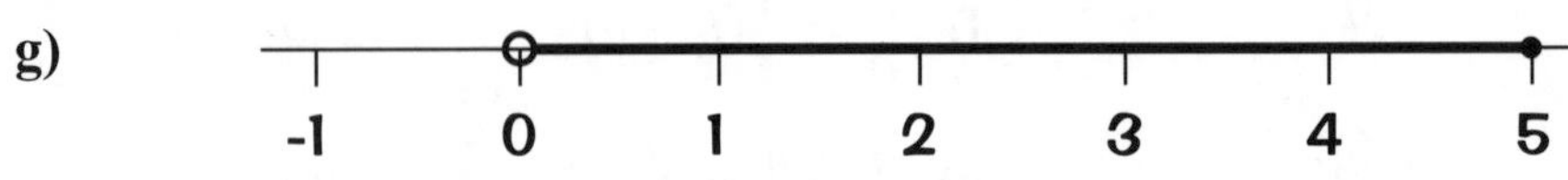

h)
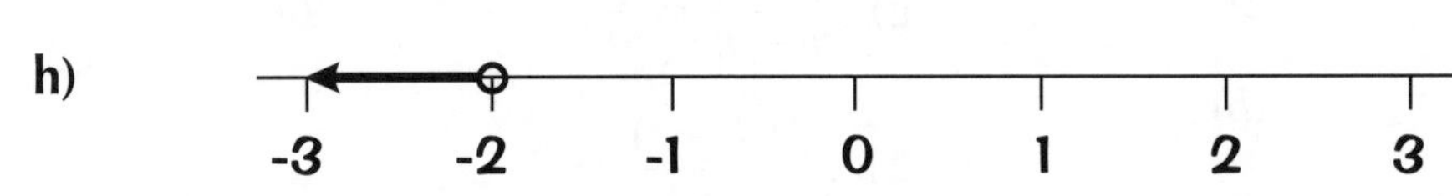

Q2 By drawing an appropriate part of the number line for each question, represent each of the following inequalities.

a) $x > 5$
b) $x \leq 2$
c) $2 > x > -5$
d) $3 > x \geq -2$
e) $3 \geq x > -2$
f) $7 \geq x > 6$
g) $-3 \leq x \leq -2$
h) $0 \geq x > -3$

Q3 Solve the following:

a) $3x + 2 > 11$
b) $5x + 4 < 24$
c) $5x + 7 \leq 32$
d) $3x + 12 \leq 30$
e) $2x - 7 \geq 8$
f) $17 + 4x < 33$
g) $2(x + 3) < 20$
h) $2(5x - 4) < 32$
i) $5(x + 2) \geq 25$
j) $4(x - 1) > 40$
k) $10 - 2x > 4x - 8$
l) $7 - 2x \leq 4x + 10$
m) $8 - 3x \geq 14$
n) $16 - x < 11$
o) $16 - x > 1$
p) $12 - 3x \leq 18$

Inequalities

Q4 Find the largest integer x, such that $2x + 5 \geq 5x - 2$.

Q5 When a number is subtracted from 11, and this new number is then divided by two, the result is always less than five. Write this information as an inequality and solve it to show the possible values of the number.

Q6 Two schools are merging and a new school is being built to accommodate all the pupils. There will be 1,130 pupils in total in the new school. No class must have more than 32 pupils. How many classrooms are needed? Show this information as an inequality.

Call the number of classrooms x.

Q7 A couple are planning their wedding. For the reception in a local hotel, they have a budget of £900. If the hotel charges £18 per head, how many guests could be invited? Show this information as an inequality.

Q8 The shaded region satisfies three inequalities. Write down these inequalities.

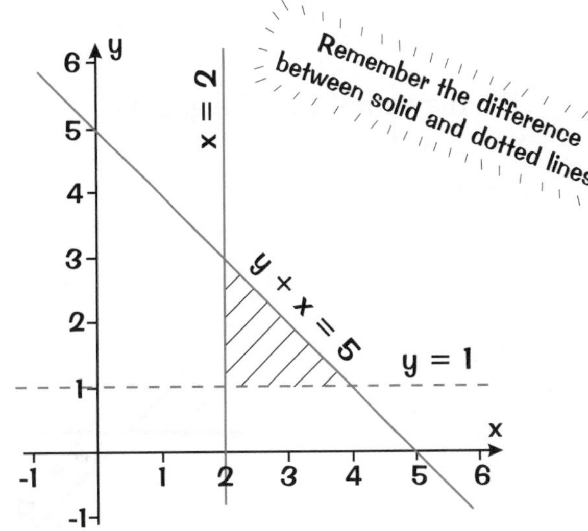

Q9 Draw a set of axes with the x-axis from –2 to 6 and the y-axis from –1 to 7. Show on a graph the region enclosed by the following three inequalities.

$$y < 6, \qquad x + y \geq 5 \qquad \text{and} \qquad x \leq 5$$

Q10 Draw a set of axes with the x-axis from –4 to 5 and the y-axis from –3 to 6. Show on a graph the region enclosed by the following.

$$y \leq 2x + 4, \qquad y < 5 - x \qquad \text{and} \qquad y \geq \frac{x}{3} - 1$$

Q11 A company are recruiting new members of staff. All applicants must take two online tests. To get an interview, applicants must score higher than 5 on the first test, at least 7 on the second, and have a total combined score of at least 14.

a) Write out three inequalities to represent the three criteria for getting an interview. Use x for the score on the first test and y for the score on the second test.

b) The company want to analyse the quality of applicants by plotting their test scores on a graph, and picking out the ones who satisfy the criteria. Using suitable axes, show on a graph the region enclosed by the three inequalities where suitable candidates would be placed.

Simultaneous Equations and Graphs

Q1 Solve the following simultaneous equations by drawing graphs. Use values $0 \leqslant x \leqslant 6$

a) $y = x$
$y = 9 - 2x$

b) $y = 2x + 1$
$2y = 8 + x$

c) $y = 4 - 2x$
$x + y = 3$

d) $y = 3 - x$
$3x + y = 5$

e) $2x + y = 6$
$y = 3x + 1$

f) $y = 2x$
$y = x + 1$

g) $x + y = 5$
$2x - 1 = y$

h) $2y = 3x$
$y = x + 1$

i) $y = x - 3$
$y + x = 7$

j) $y = x + 1$
$2x + y = 10$

Q2 The diagram shows the graphs:
$y = 2x + 2$
$y = 8$
$y = -2x + 4$

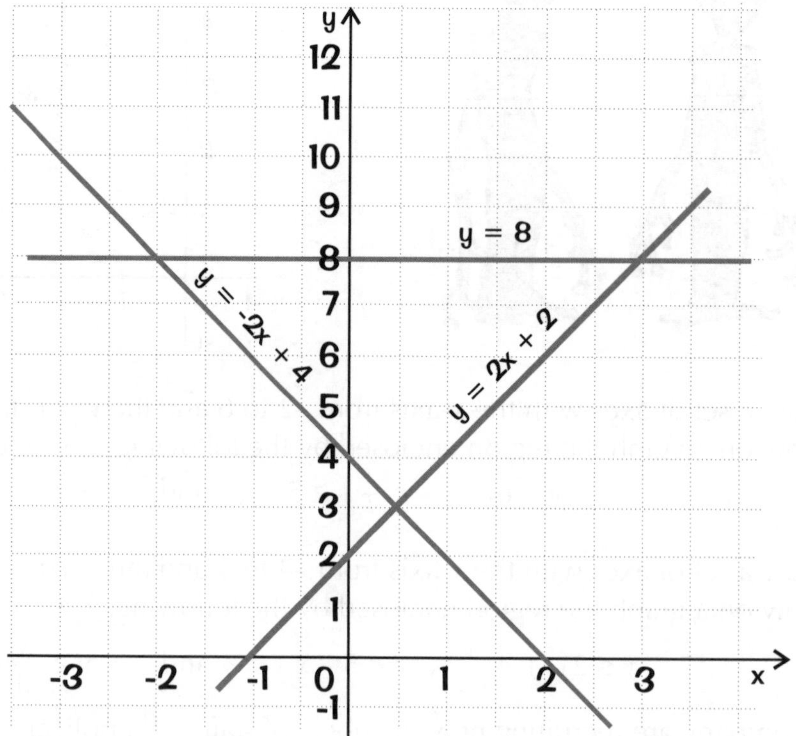

Use the graphs to find the solutions to:

a) $4 = -2x$

b) $-2x + 4 = 2x + 2$

c) $2 + 4x - 4 = 0$

d) $8 = 2x + 2$

Simultaneous Equations

To solve simultaneous equations from scratch, you've got to get rid of either x or y first — to leave you with an equation with just one unknown in it.

Q1 Solve the following simultaneous equations:

a) $4x + 6y = 16$
$x + 2y = 5$

b) $3x + 8y = 24$
$x + y = 3$

c) $3y - 8x = 24$
$3y + 2x = 9$

Q2 Two farmers are buying livestock at a market. Farmer Ed buys 6 sheep and 5 pigs for £430 and Farmer Jacob buys 4 sheep and 10 pigs for £500.

a) If sheep cost £x and pigs cost £y, write down the two purchases as a pair of simultaneous equations.

b) Solve for x and y.

Q3 On Farmer Ed's farm, the cats have got into the chicken coop and are causing chaos. Falmer Ed counts, in total, 11 heads and 30 legs. How many cats and how many chickens are in the chicken coop?

Q4 Isobel is buying pick & mix sweets. She weighs out 20 jellies and 30 toffees which come to 230 g. She takes one of each off the scales before they get bagged up, and the weight drops to 221 g. How much does an individual toffee weigh?

Q5 Find the value of x and y for each of the following rectangles, by first writing down a pair of simultaneous equations and then solving them.

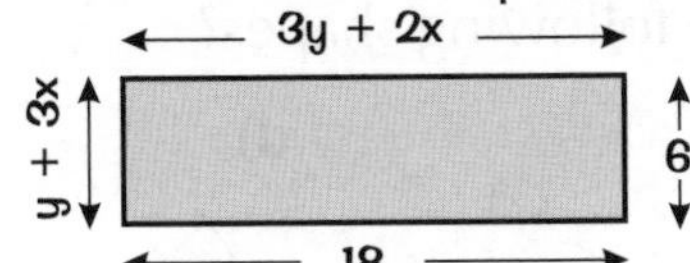

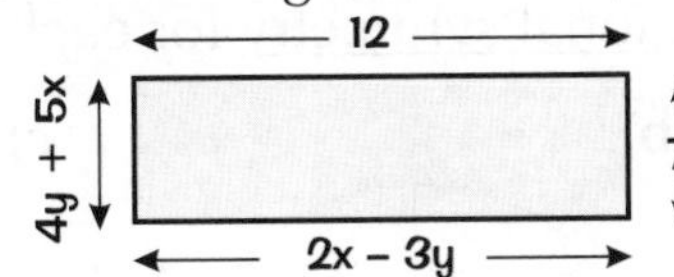

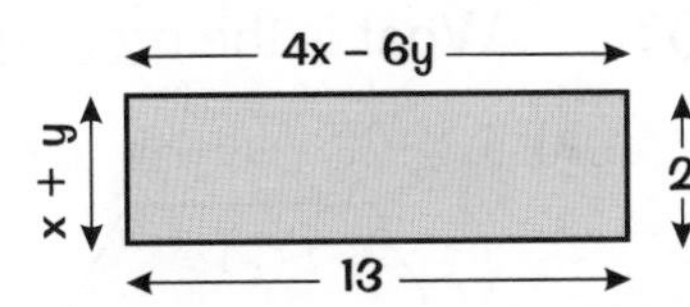

Q6 Two customers enter a shop to buy milk and cornflakes. Mrs Smith buys 5 pints of milk and 2 boxes of cornflakes and spends £3.44. Mr Brown buys 4 pints of milk and 3 boxes of cornflakes and receives £6.03 change after paying with a £10 note. Write down a pair of simultaneous equations and solve them to find the price in pence of a pint of milk (m) and a box of cornflakes (c).

Q7 Solve $\dfrac{3(x-y)}{5} = x - 3y = x - 6$.

Symmetry

They do say that bad things happen in threes... and now you've got to learn three types of symmetry — but don't worry, I reckon their names pretty much give the game away.

There are THREE types of symmetry:	
1) LINE SYMMETRY	You can draw a mirror line across the object and both sides will fold together exactly.
2) PLANE SYMMETRY	This applies to 3-D solids. You can draw a plane mirror surface through the solid to make the shape exactly the same on both sides of the plane.
3) ROTATIONAL SYMMETRY	You can rotate the shape or drawing into different positions that all look exactly the same.

Q1 Draw <u>all</u> the lines of symmetry for each of the following shapes. (Some shapes may have no lines of symmetry)

a) **b)** **c)** **d)** **e)** **f)**

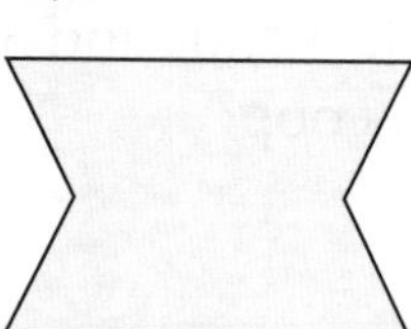

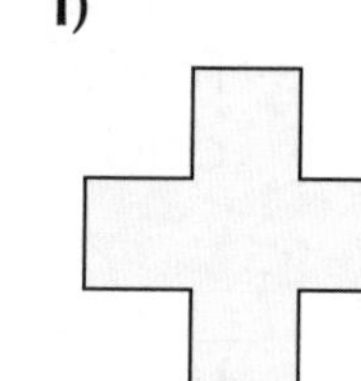

These questions are a piece of cake if you use tracing paper — you can use it in the Exam, so remember to ask for it.

Q2 What is the <u>order of rotational symmetry</u> for each of the following shapes?

a)

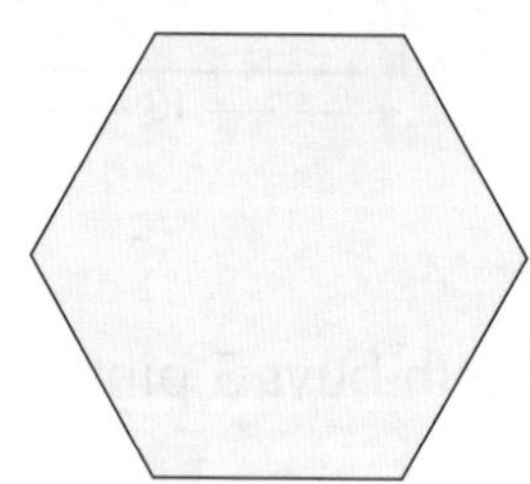

b)

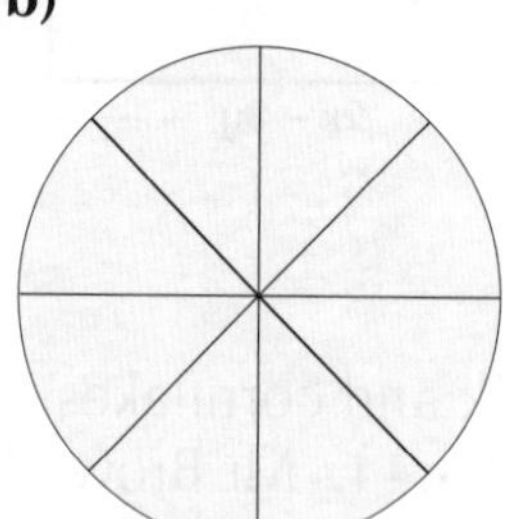

c)

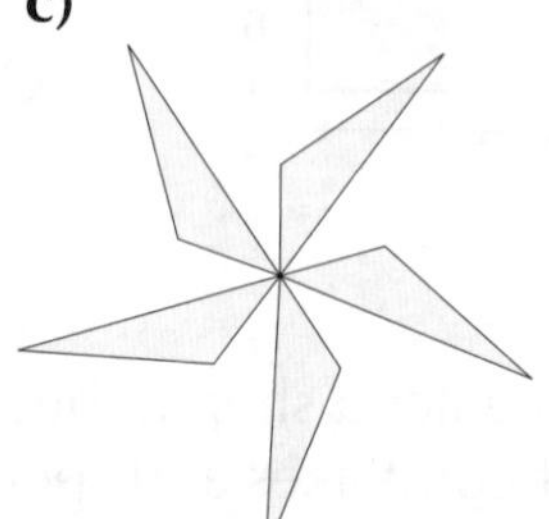

d)

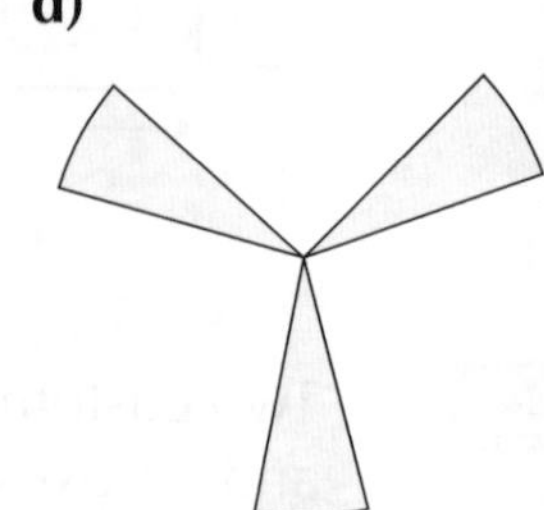

Q3 Mark in the <u>lines of symmetry</u> of the following letters. State the <u>order</u> of rotational symmetry for each one.

Symmetry

Watch out for those 3-D solids and planes of symmetry — they're pretty hard to draw, so make sure you do this page in pencil — and have a rubber ready...

Q4 Here is a cuboid:

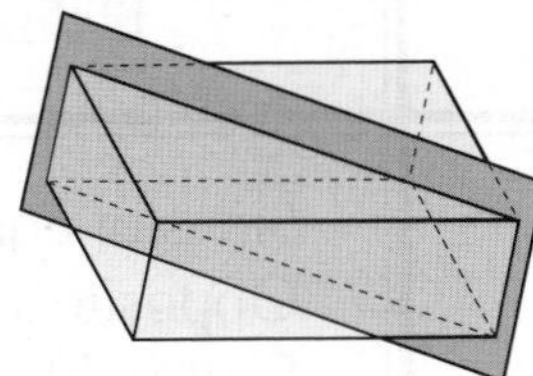

Is the plane a plane of symmetry?

Q5 How many planes of symmetry does this <u>triangular prism</u> have?

Q6 How many planes of symmetry does a <u>circular cone</u> have?

Q7 In the square-based pyramid shown, is this a plane of symmetry?

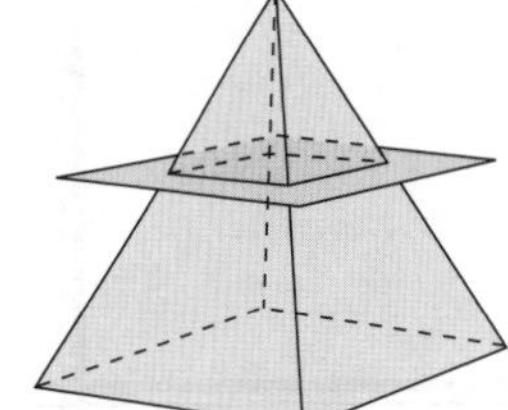

Q8 Draw in another plane of symmetry, which is <u>perpendicular</u> to the one drawn in the diagram.

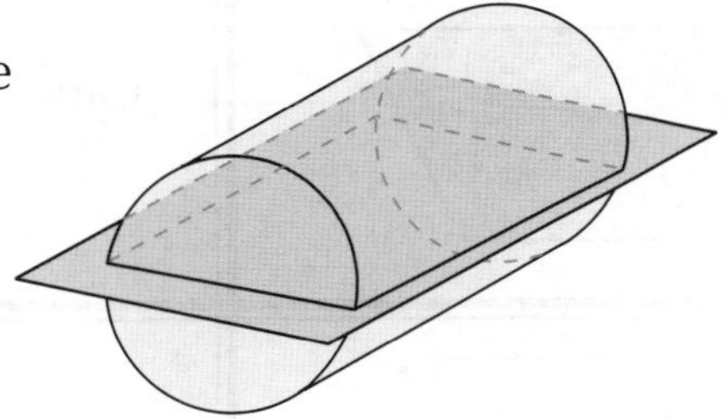

Q9 Would all the planes of symmetry of a cube meet in a <u>line</u>, <u>point</u> or <u>plane</u>?

Q10 A roofing tile is shown.

a) How many planes of symmetry does it have?

b) What <u>angle</u> do they meet at?

c) <u>How</u> do they meet — in a line or plane, or at a point?

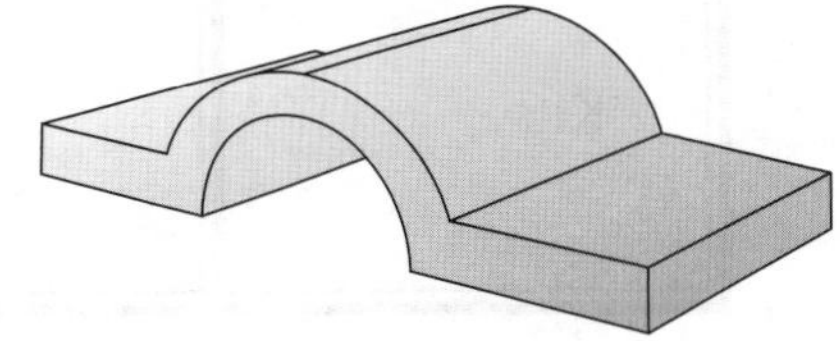

Q11 The diagram shows a <u>square-based pyramid</u> of height X with a square base of side 2X. P is the centre of the base, whilst T is the mid-point of AB, and S is the midpoint of CD.

a) How many planes of symmetry does the square-based pyramid have?

b) Is it true that ∠TVS is a <u>right angle</u>?

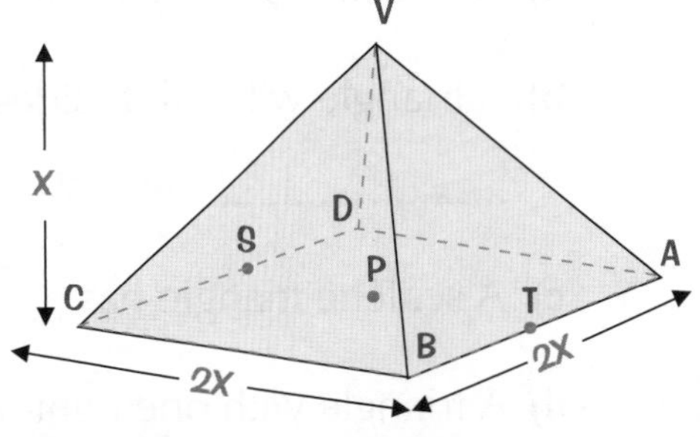

The Shapes you Need to Know

Q1 Fill in the blanks in the table.

NAME	DRAWING	DESCRIPTION
Square		Sides of equal length. Opposite sides parallel. Four right angles.
....	....	Opposite sides parallel and the same length. Four right angles.
....		Opposite sides are .... and equal. Opposite angles are equal.
Trapezium		Only .... sides are parallel.
Rhombus		A parallelogram but with all sides ....
Kite	....	Two pairs of adjacent equal sides.

Q2 Fill in the gaps in these sentences.

a) An isosceles triangle has .... equal sides and .... equal angles.

b) A triangle with all its sides equal and all its angles equal is called an .... triangle.

c) A scalene triangle has .... equal sides and .... equal angles.

d) A triangle with one right-angle is called a .... triangle.

Shapes and Angles

Estimating angles is easy once you know the 4 special angles — you can use them as reference points.

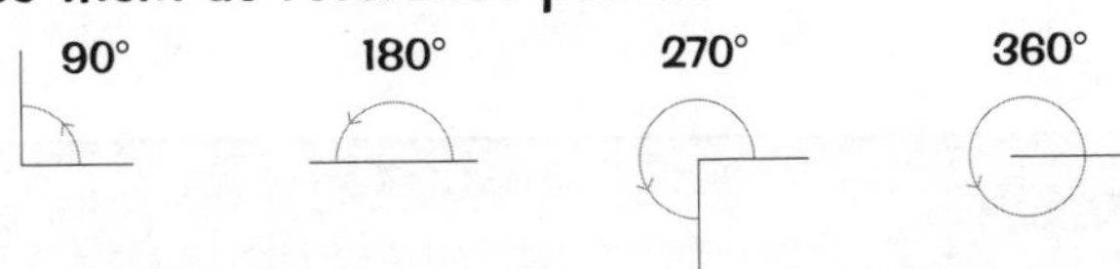

Q1 For each of the angles below write down its type, estimate its size (before you measure it!) and finally measure each angle with a protractor. The first one has been done for you.

Angle	Type	Estimated Size	Actual Size
a	acute	40°	43°
b			
c			
d			
e			
f			

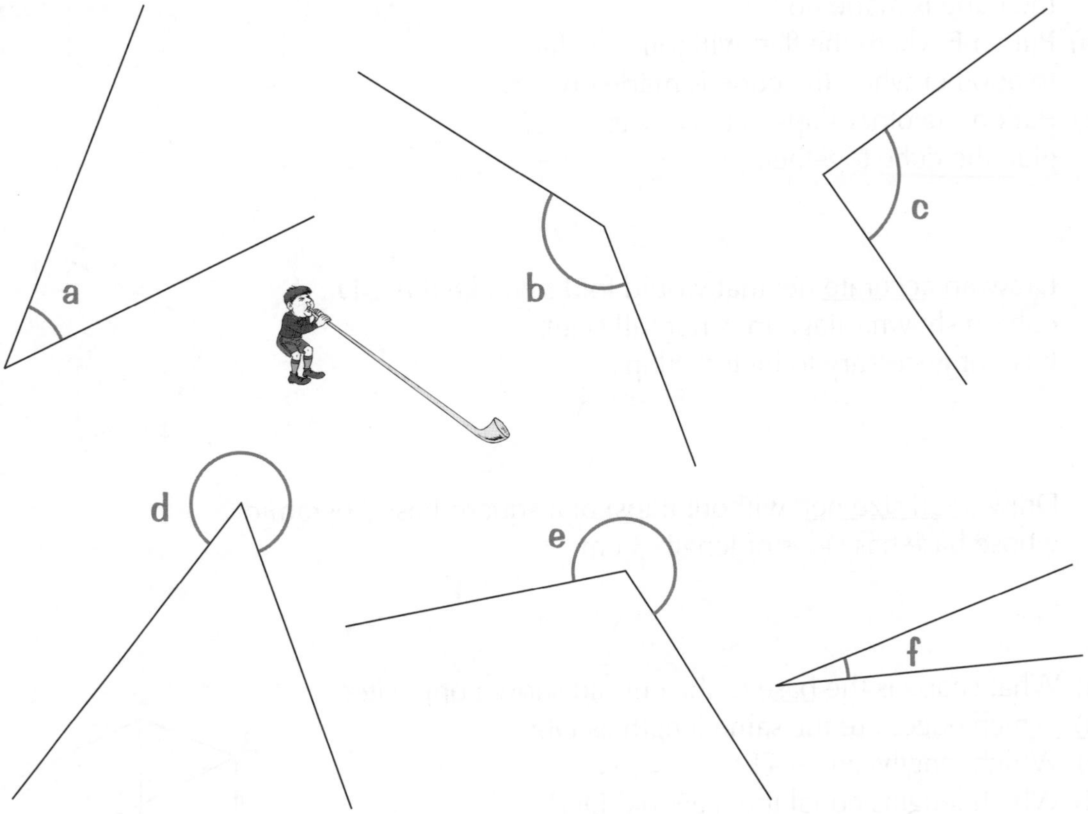

a b c d e f

Q2 Stephen is measuring the angles inside a parallelogram for his maths homework. To save time, he measures just one and works out what the other angles must be from this. If the angle he measures is 52°, what are the other three?

Nets and Projections

Before you go any further — make sure you know these 3 facts...

Surface Area and Nets

1) SURFACE AREA only applies to solid 3-D objects. It's the TOTAL AREA of all the OUTER SURFACES added together.
2) A NET is just A SOLID SHAPE folded out FLAT.
3) SURFACE AREA OF SOLID = AREA OF NET.

There are 4 nets that you need to know inside out... so to speak: 1) Triangular Prism, 2) Cube, 3) Cuboid, 4) Pyramid. I reckon you shouldn't read any further till you're 100% happy with them.

Q1 The net shown will fold to make a cube. Only one flap is shown. Copy the diagram.

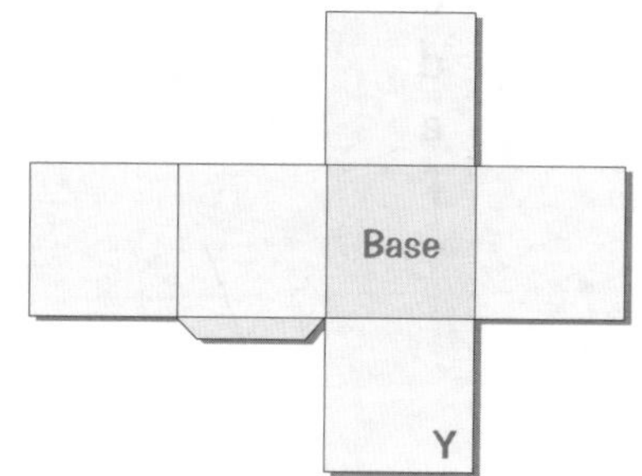

a) Put an X in each corner that touches Y when the cube is made up.

b) Put an F where the flap will join one face to another when the cube is made up.

c) Put on the other flaps necessary to glue the cube together.

Q2 Draw an accurate net that would fold to make the 3-D cuboid shown (diagram is not full size). It is not necessary to include flaps.

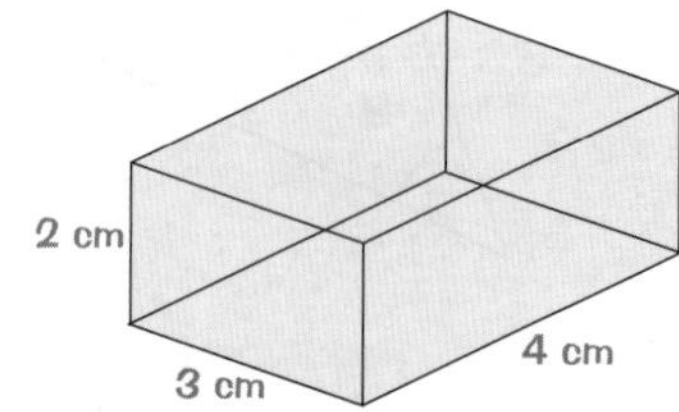

Q3 Draw a full size net (without flaps) of a square-based pyramid whose base has sides of length 3 cm.

Q4 **a)** What shape is the base of the cuboid shown opposite?

b) Which edges are the same length as DE?

c) Which lengths equal CE?

d) Which lengths equal the diagonal DG?

e) How many vertices does the cuboid have?

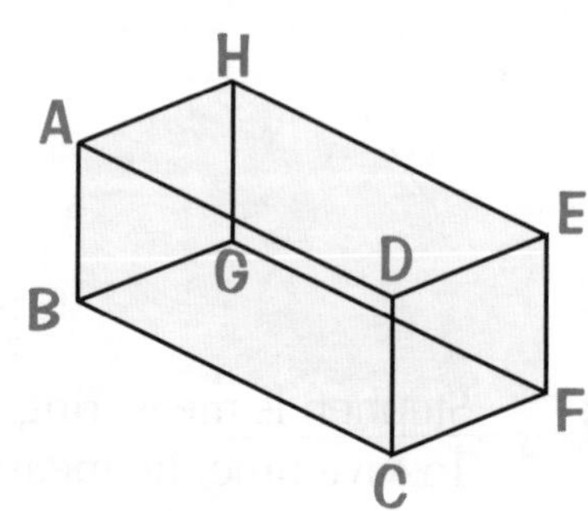

Q5 Draw a circular cone.

a) How many vertices does it have?

b) How many edges?

Nets and Projections

Q6

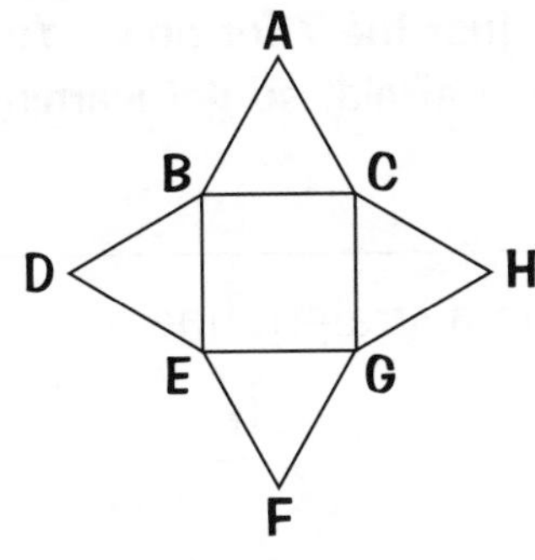

The diagram shows the net of a solid in which ABC is an equilateral triangle and BCGE is a square.

a) Which points will coincide with A when the net is folded up to make the solid?

b) Describe the symmetry of the net.

c) How many faces, edges and vertices does it have when in solid form?

Q7 The diagram shows the net of a cube of edge 8 cm.

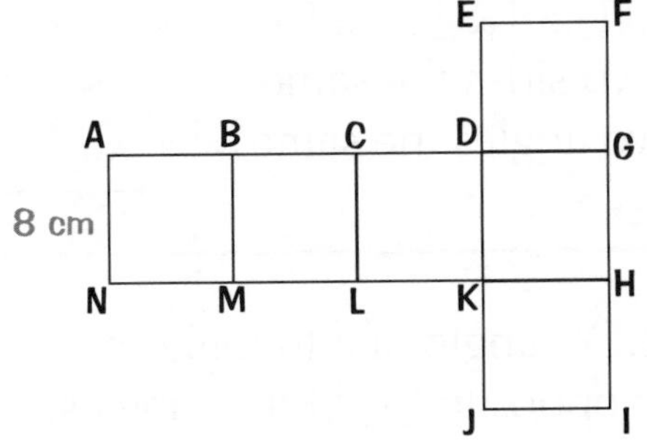

a) Which point coincides with M when the net is folded to make the cube?

b) Find the area of the face DGHK.

c) What is the total surface area of the cube?

d) Draw a 3-D scale drawing of the completed cube.

Q8

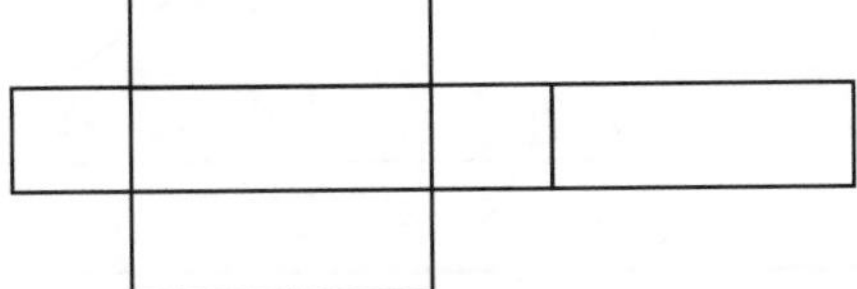

This diagram shows a net for a rectangular box with a lid. For the same box sketch a different net.

Q9 Which of these two nets will form a pyramid on a triangular base with all four faces equilateral triangles?

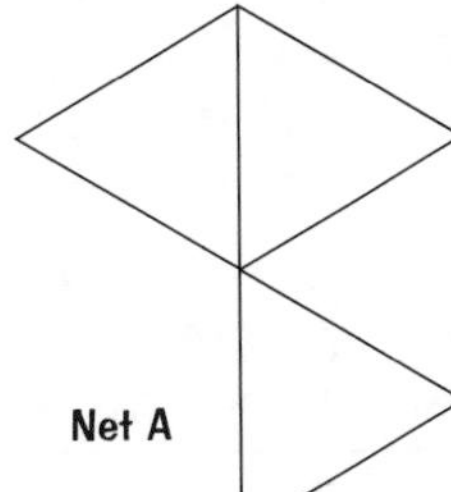

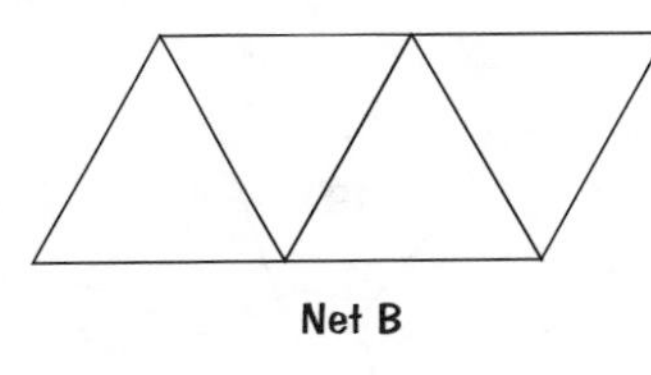

Q10 The diagram shows an isometric projection of a triangular prism.

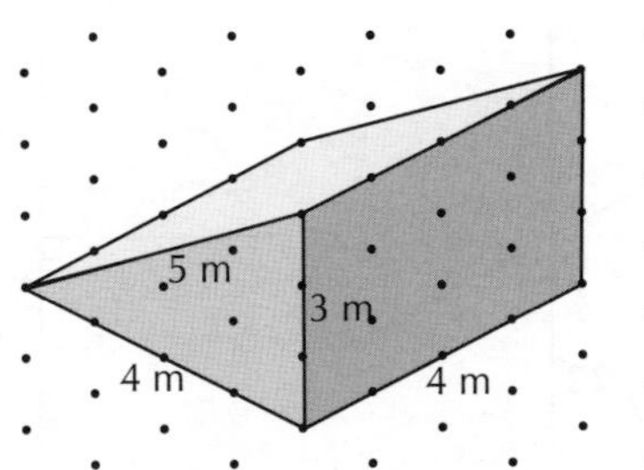

Draw:

a) the front elevation

b) the side elevation

c) the plan.

Geometry

Here are some angle rules then — just the 7 for now. You can't get away without knowing these, I'm afraid, so get learning.

1) Angles in a triangle add up to 180°

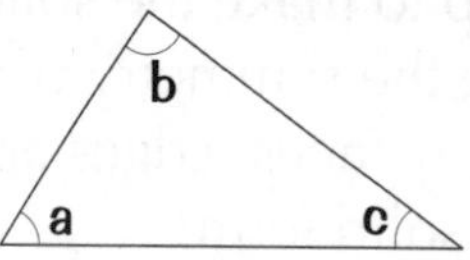

2) Angles in a 4-sided shape add up to 360°

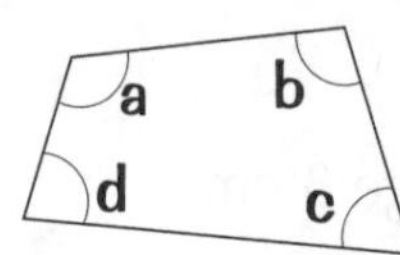

3) Angles round a point add up to 360°

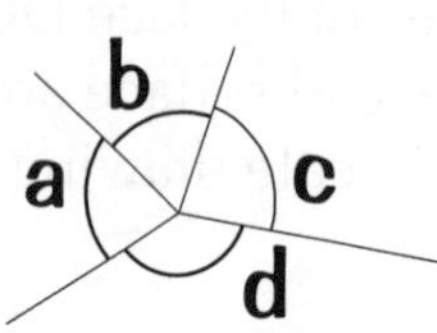

4) When a line crosses TWO PARALLEL LINES, the two bunches of angles are the same

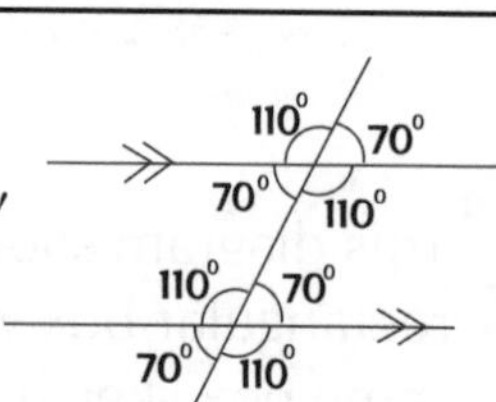

5) Angles on a straight line add up to 180°

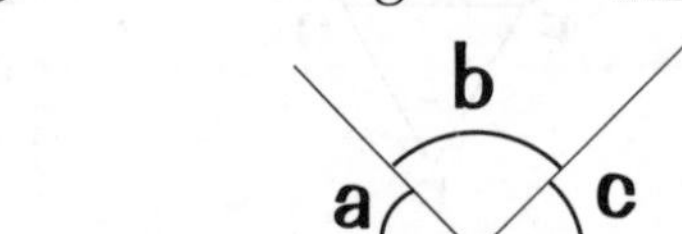

6) ISOSCELES TRIANGLES have two sides the same and two angles the same

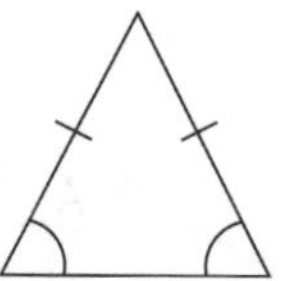

7) EXTERIOR angle of a triangle = sum of opposite INTERIOR angles.

d = a + b

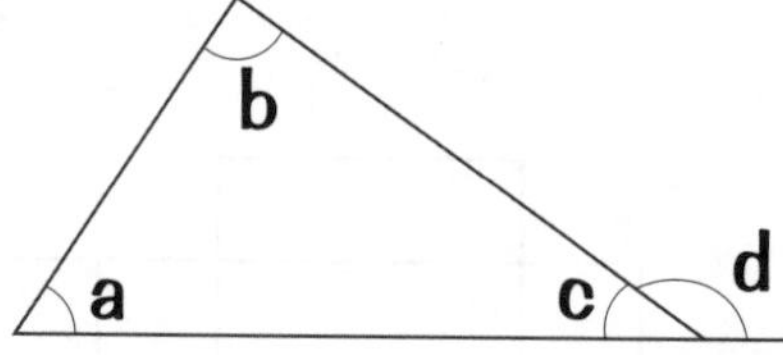

For the following diagrams, find the lettered angles. LM is a straight line.

Q1 a)

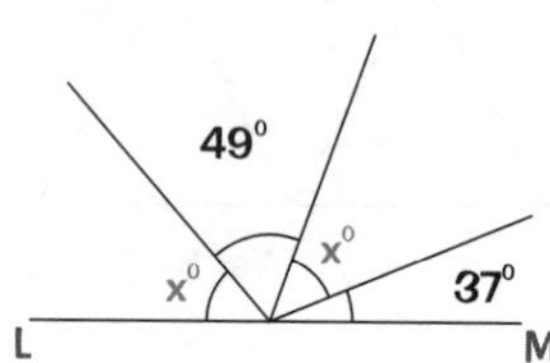

b)

c)

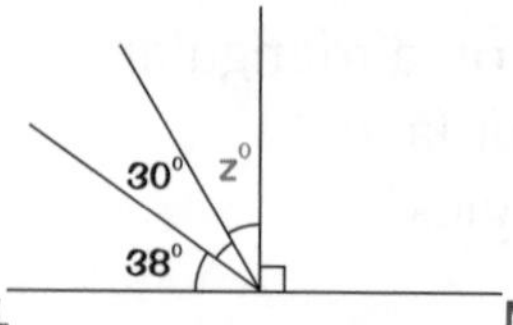

d)

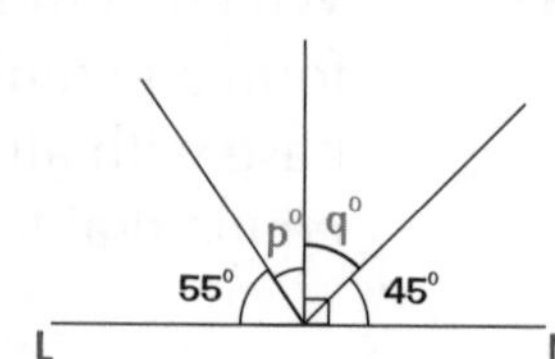

Q2 a)

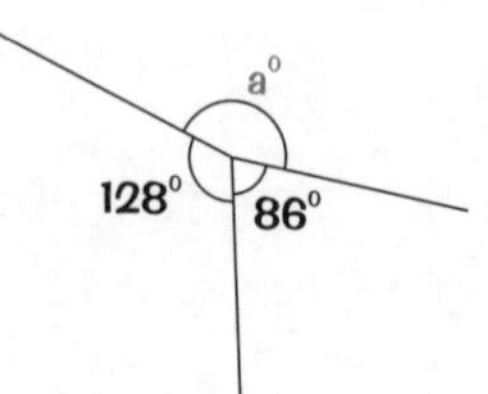

b)

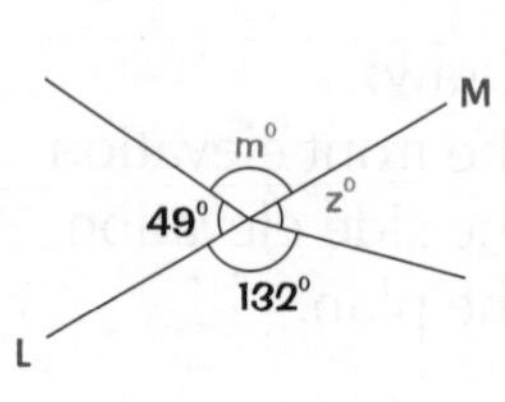

c)

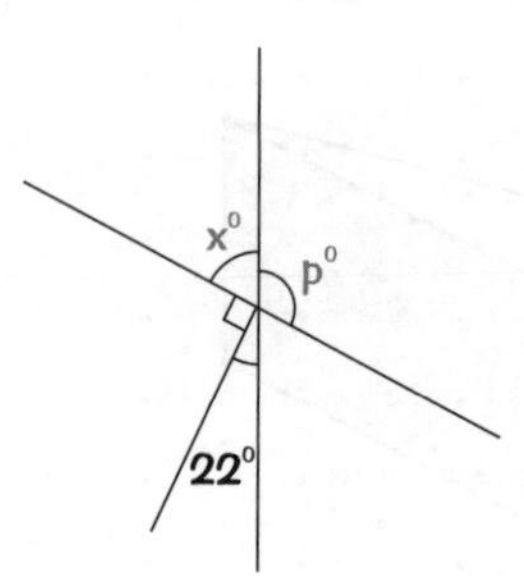

d)

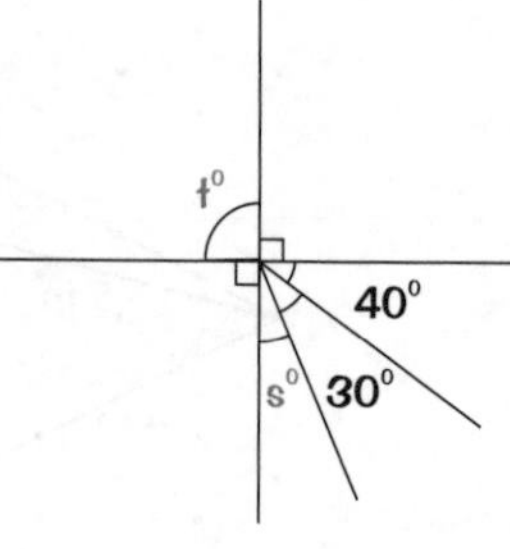

Geometry

This page is a bit dull — just lots of boring angles... still, that's geometry for you. Oh and by the way, you've got to work the angles out — don't try and sneakily measure them, they're probably drawn wrong anyway...

For the following diagrams, find the lettered angles. LM is a straight line.

Q3 a)

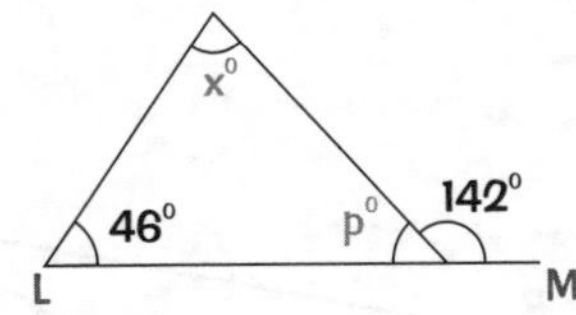

b)

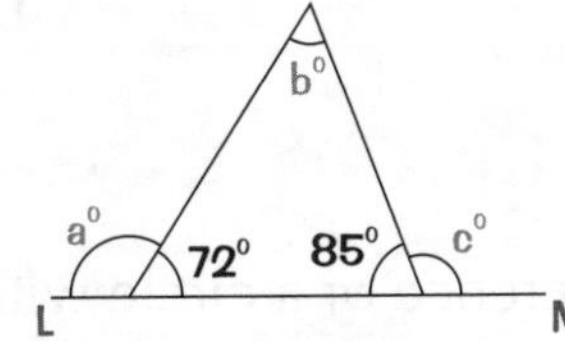

c)

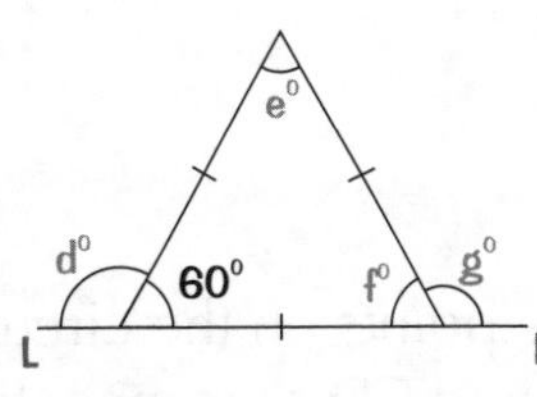

d)

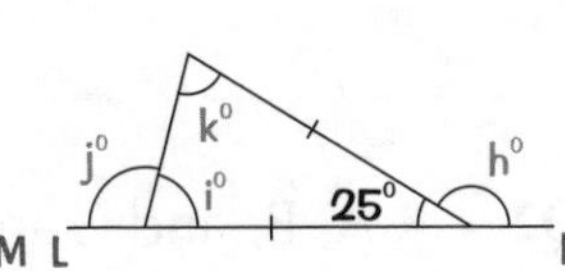

Q4 a)

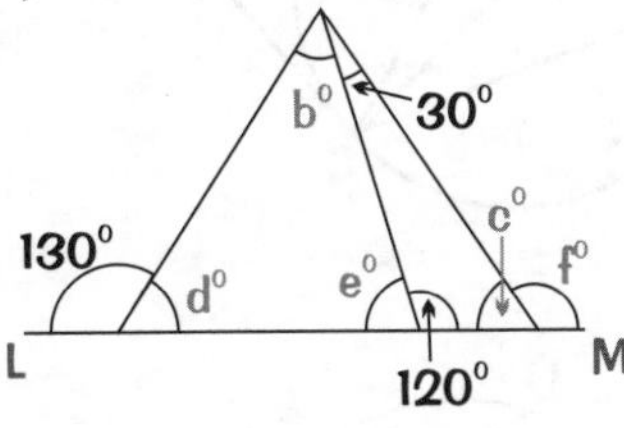

b)

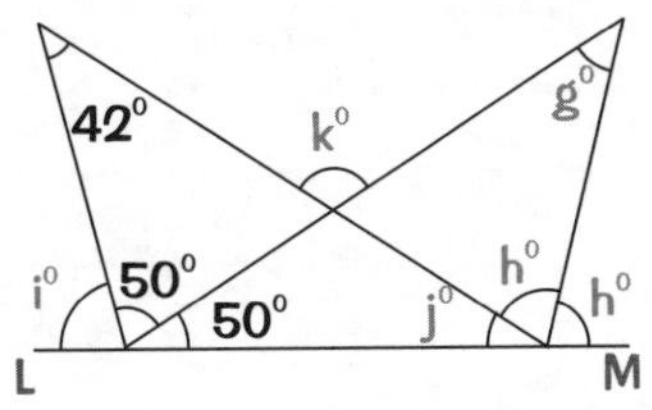

c)

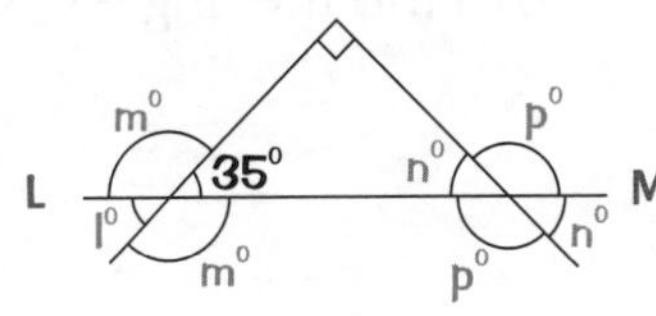

Keep an eye out for parallel lines — they'll help no end... as long as you can remember the angle rules, of course.

Q5 a)

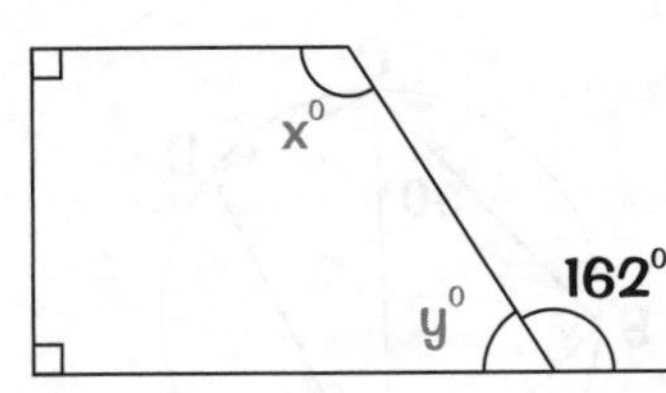

b)

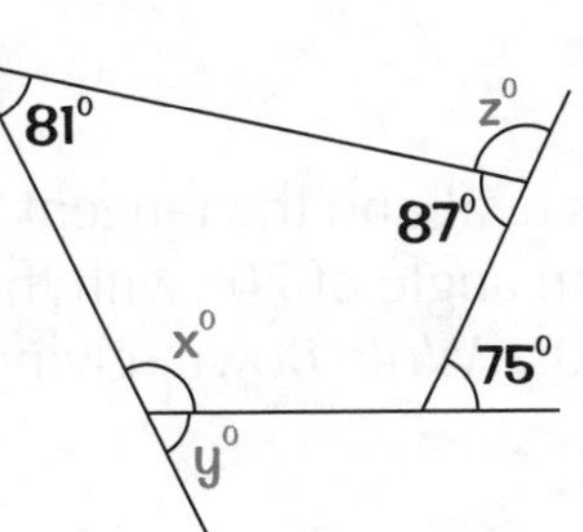

c)

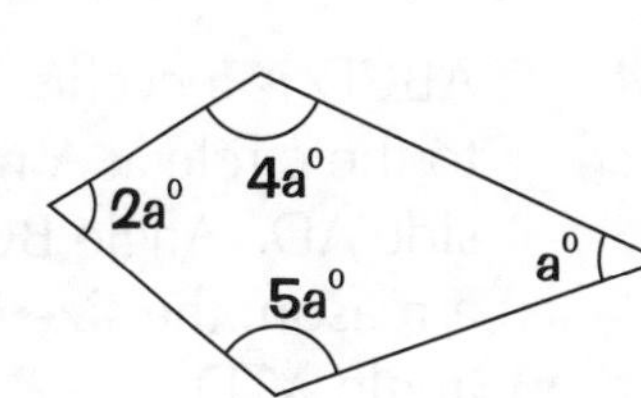

Q6 a)

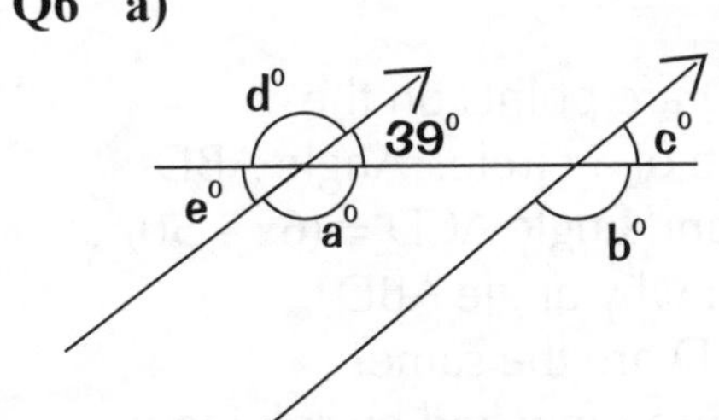

b)

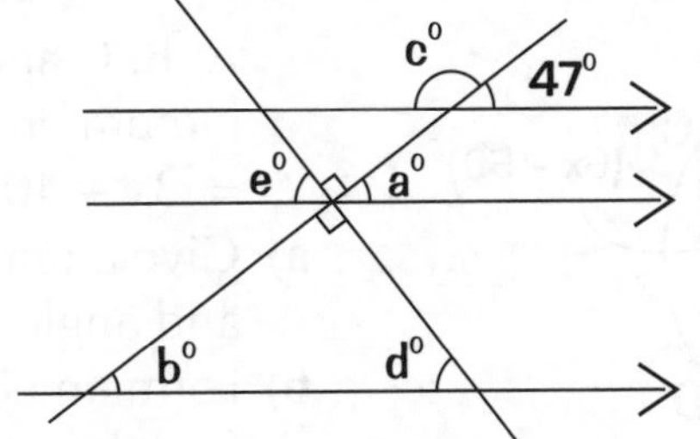

c)

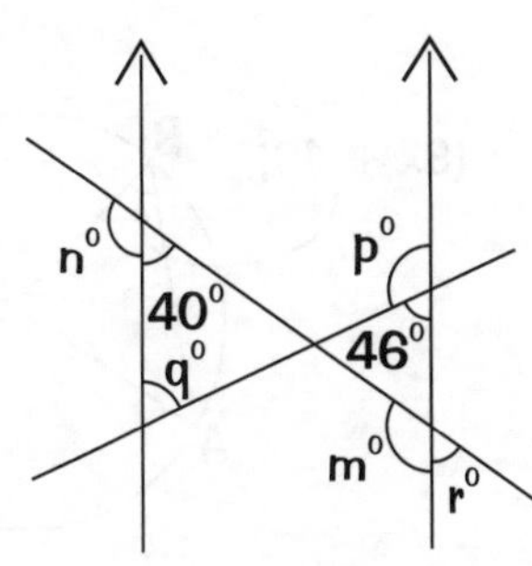

Circle Geometry

Q1 ABCD is a cyclic quadrilateral with angle BCD = 100°.
EF is a tangent to the circle touching it at A.
Angle DAF = 30°.
Write down the size of angle:

a) BAD
b) EAB.

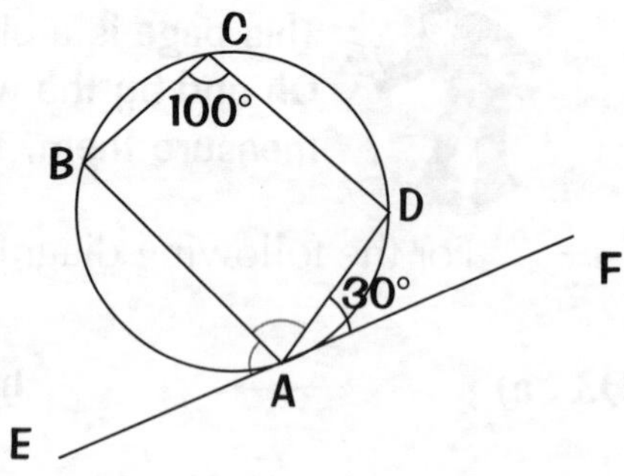

Q2 A, B, and C are points on the circumference of a circle with centre O. BD and CD are tangents of the circle.

a) State the length BD.
b) Calculate the angle COD.
c) State the angle COB.
d) Find the angle CAB.

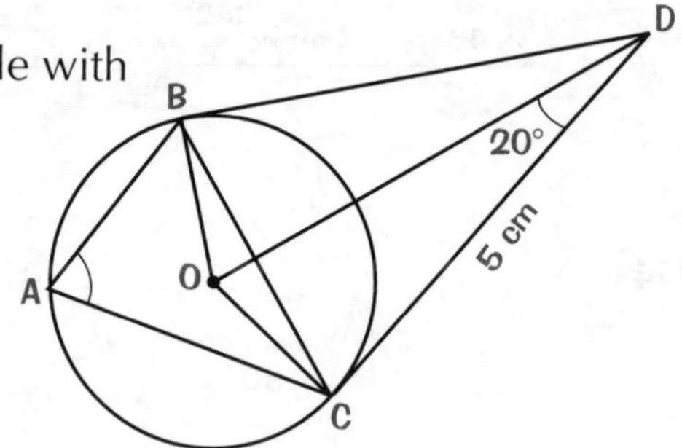

Q3 A, B, C, D and E are points on the circumference of a circle with centre O. Angle BDE = 53°. The line AF is a tangent to the circle, touching it at A.
Angle EAF = 32°. Find:

a) angle BOE
b) angle ACE.

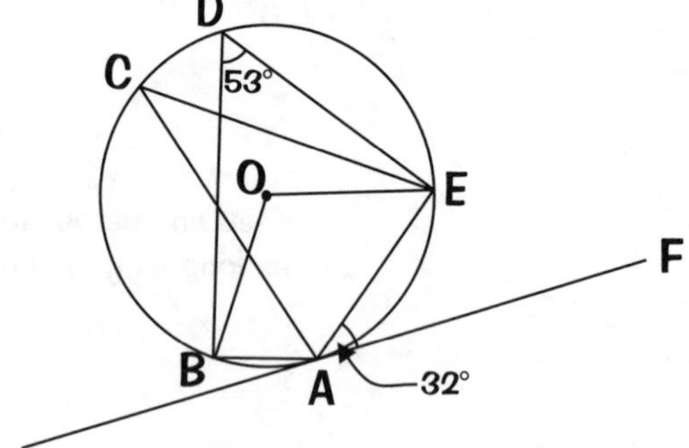

Q4 ABCD is a cyclic quadrilateral and the tangent to the circle at A makes an angle of 70° with the side AD. Angle BCA = 30°. Write down, giving a reason, the size of:

a) angle ACD
b) angle BAD.

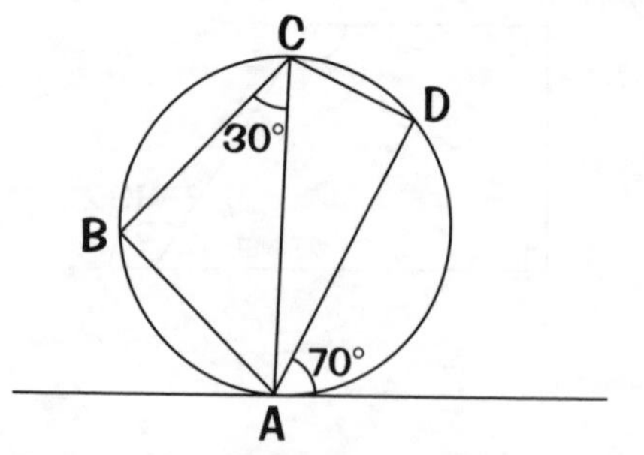

Q5

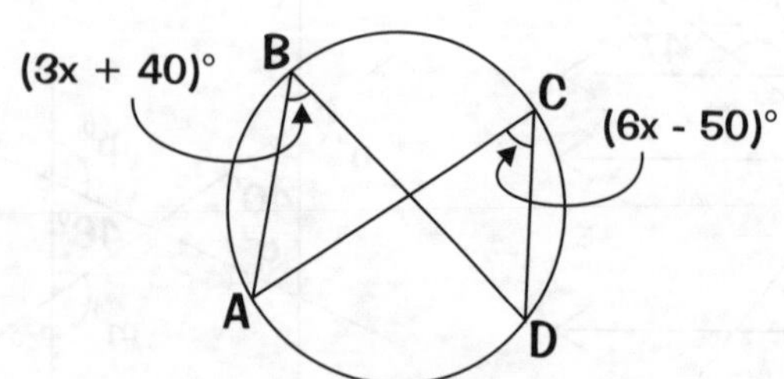

A, B, C and D are points on the circumference of a circle. Angle ABD = $(3x + 40)°$ and angle ACD = $(6x - 50)°$.

a) Give a reason why angle ABD and angle ACD are the same.
b) Form an equation in x and by solving it, find the size of angle ABD.

Circle Geometry

Q6 A, B, C and D are points on the circumference of a circle. O is the centre of the circle and angle AOD = 140°. Write down:

a) angle ABD
b) angle ABC
c) angle DBC.

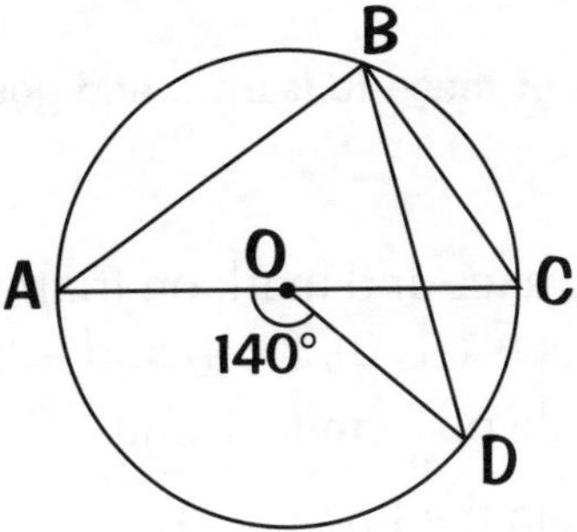

Q7 A tangent of a circle is drawn, touching it at A. C and B are two other points on the circumference and AOB is a diameter. O is the centre of the circle. Angle ABC is 23°.

a) Write down the size of angle ACB, giving a reason for your answer.
b) Find the size of the angle marked x° in the diagram.

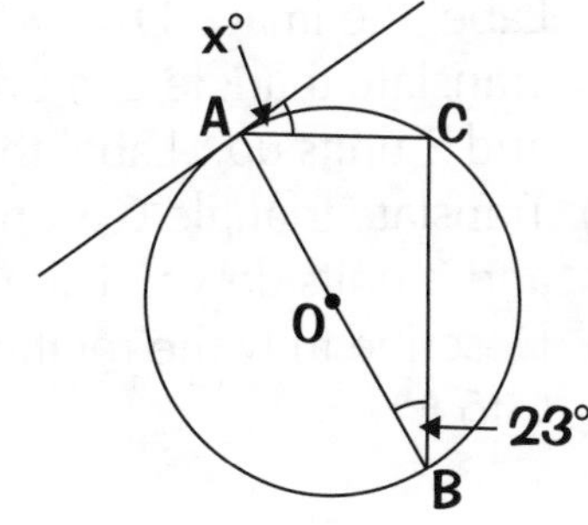

Q8

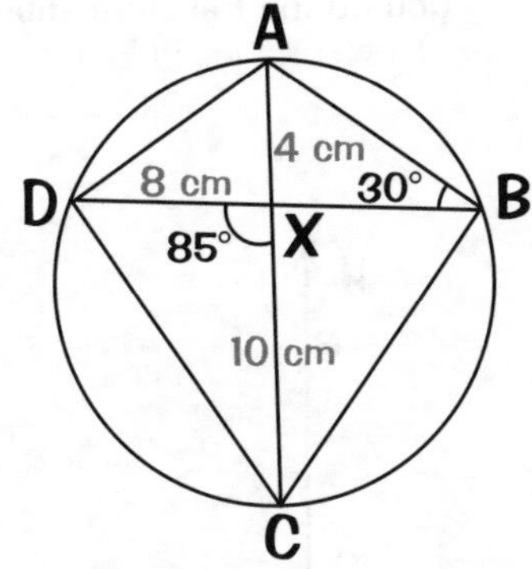

ABCD is a cyclic quadrilateral. The lines AC and BD intersect at X. Lengths AX = 4 cm, DX = 8 cm and XC = 10 cm. Angles DXC = 85° and ABD = 30°.

a) Show that triangles DXC and AXB are similar.
b) Find the length of XB.
c) Write down the size of angle BDC.

Q9 B, C and D are three points on the circumference of a circle with BD as a diameter. O is the centre of the circle and ADC is a straight line.
AB = 10 cm and BC = 3 cm.
Write down the size of angle ACB, giving a reason for your answer.

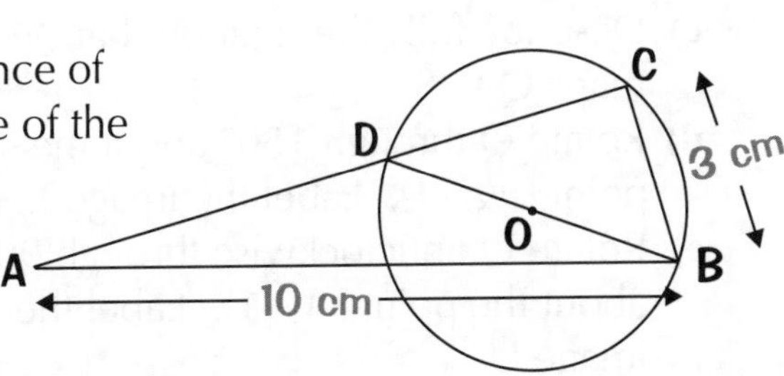

The Four Transformations

Only 4 of these to learn... and good old TERRY's always around to help if you need him.

Q1 Copy the axes and mark on triangle A with corners (-1, 2), (0, 4) and (-2, 4). Use a scale of 1 cm to 1 unit.

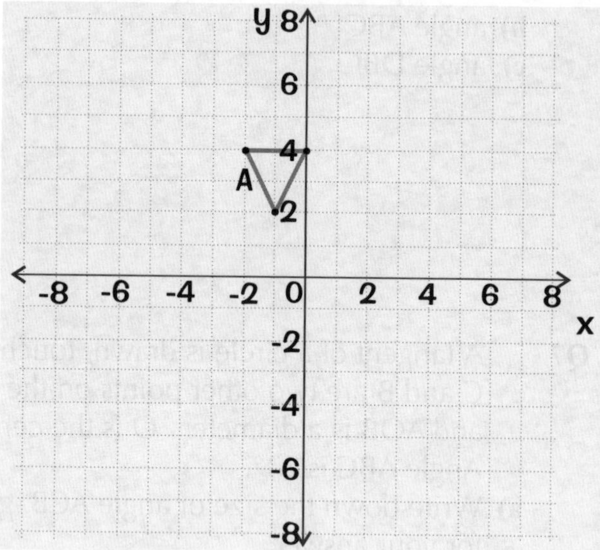

a) Reflect A in the line $y = -x$. Label this image B.
b) Reflect A in the line $x = 1$. Label the image C.
c) Reflect A in the line $y = -1$. Label the image D.
d) Translate triangle D 4 units to the right and 2 units up. Label this image E.
e) Translate triangle C 3 units to the right and 3 units down. Label this image F.
f) Describe fully the rotation that sends C to E.

It helps to label the corners of the triangle so you can see exactly what goes where when you do the transformations.

Q2 Copy the axes using a scale of 1 cm to 1 unit. Mark on the axes a quadrilateral Q with corners (-2, 1), (-3, 1), (-3, 3) and (-2, 3).

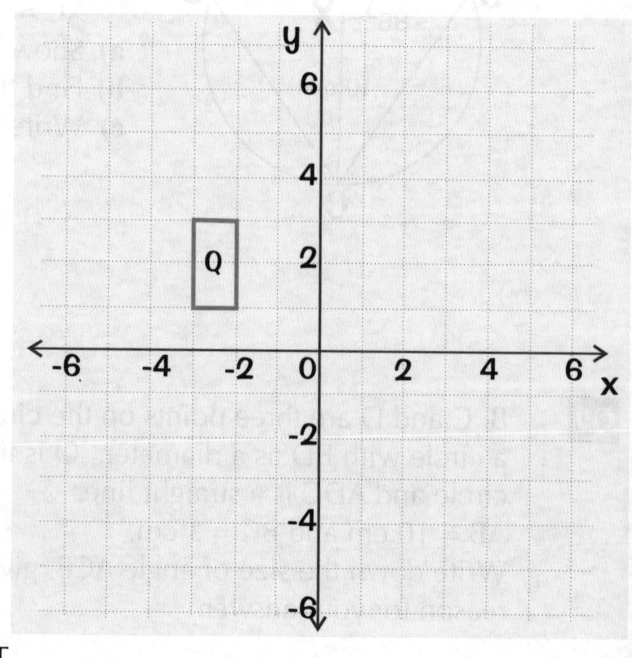

a) Rotate Q clockwise through 90° about the point (-1, 2). Label the image R.
b) Rotate R clockwise through 90° about the point (0, 1). Label the image S.
c) Describe fully the rotation that maps Q to S.
d) Rotate Q through 180° about the point (-½, -1). Label the image T.
e) Rotate Q anticlockwise through 90° about the point (-1, -1). Label the image U.
f) Describe fully the rotation that sends U to T.

The Four Transformations

Move each point separately — then check your shape hasn't done anything unexpected while you weren't looking.

Q3 Copy the axes below using a scale of 1 cm to 1 unit.

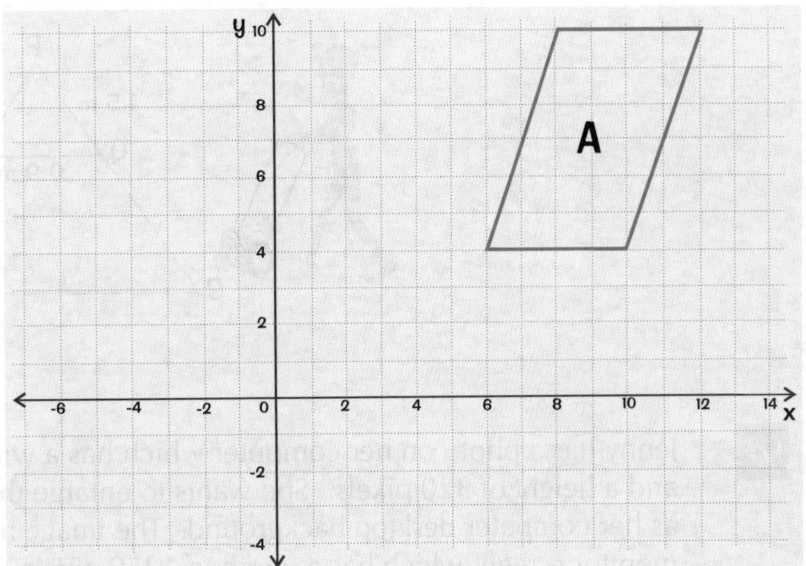

A parallelogram A has vertices at (6, 4), (10, 4), (8, 10) and (12, 10). Draw this parallelogram onto your axes. An enlargement scale factor ½ and centre (0, 0) transforms parallelogram A onto its image B.

a) Draw this image B on your axes.

b) Translate B 3 units left and 2 units down and label this image C.

c) Calculate the ratio of the area of parallelogram C to the area of parallelogram A.

Q4 A is the point (4, 3), B is (4, 1) and C is (5, 1).

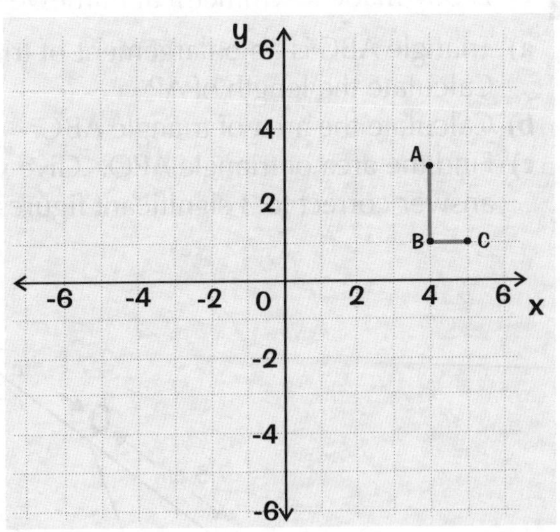

a) Using a scale of 1 cm to 1 unit draw the axes and mark on it the figure given by ABC.

b) Reflect ABC in the x-axis and label the image $A_1B_1C_1$.

c) Reflect $A_1B_1C_1$ in the y-axis and label the image $A_2B_2C_2$.

d) Describe fully the single transformation which would map ABC onto $A_2B_2C_2$.

Enlargement

Q1 The side view of a playground swing is shown in the diagram.
Triangle PST is an enlargement of triangle PQR.

a) Write down the distance PT.
b) Calculate the distance ST.

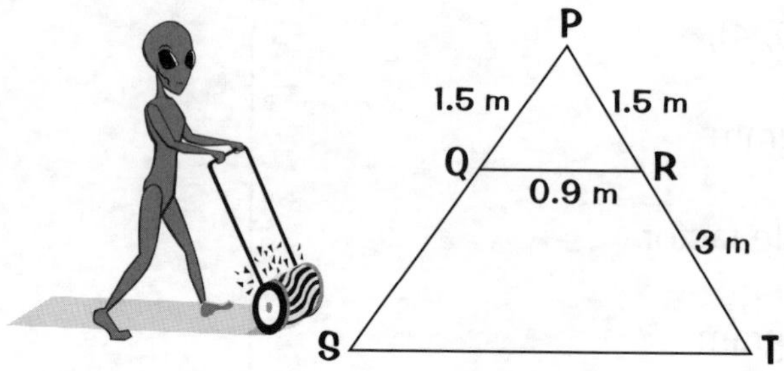

Q2 Jenny has a photo on her computer which has a width of 500 pixels and a height of 320 pixels. She wants to enlarge the photo to use as her computer desktop background. The image must fill her monitor screen, which has a width of 1250 pixels.

a) Calculate the scale factor Jenny must use to enlarge her photo.
b) Work out the height of the enlarged photo, in pixels.

Q3 A boy made a symmetrical framework with metal rods as shown below.

a) Triangle ABC is an enlargement of triangle APQ.
Calculate the length of AP.
b) Calculate the area of triangle ABC.
c) Find the area of triangle APQ. Give your answer correct to 3 significant figures.

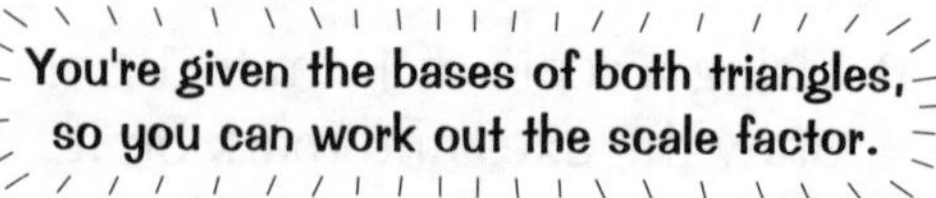

You're given the bases of both triangles,
so you can work out the scale factor.

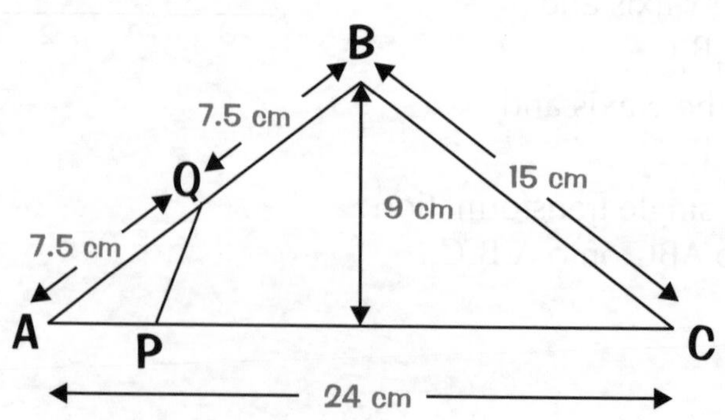

Probability

Probability can be a bit of a struggle — here's a quick reminder of the basics...

PROBABILITIES are always between 0 and 1

1) You should express probabilities as a fraction or a decimal.
2) A probability of ZERO means that it will definitely not happen.
3) A probability of ONE means it will definitely happen.

Q1 The number line opposite is a probability scale. Place the letters where you think the following statements lie, in terms of the chance of the event happening.

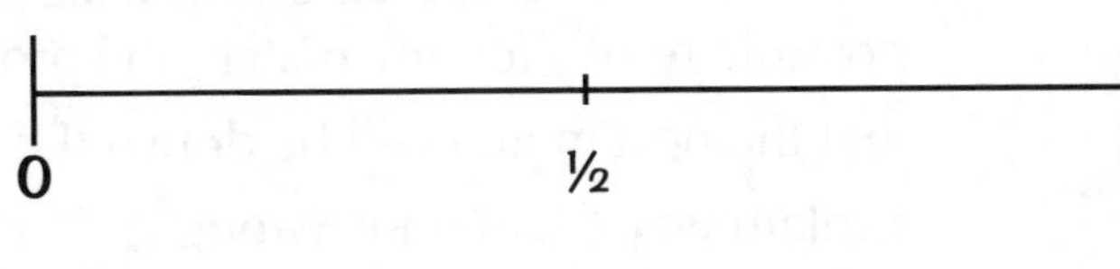

a) The probability of getting a head on a toss of a 10p piece.
b) The probability of choosing a red ball from a bag containing 2 red balls and 1 green ball.
c) The probability of shaking a five on an ordinary dice.
d) The probability of choosing a Guatemalan stamp from a bag containing 60 British stamps and 40 French stamps.

Q2 Debbie's employer organises a weekly prize draw, where the winning employee is selected at random. Debbie only joins in if her chance of winning is at least 0.1. If there are 8 other people playing this week, will Debbie choose to play?

SHORTHAND NOTATION

1) P(x) = 0.25 simply means "the probability of event x happening is 0.25".
2) Eg: if you roll a dice, the probability of rolling a 6 will be written as P(rolls a 6).

Q3 After 49 tosses of an unbiased coin, 24 have been heads and 25 have been tails. What is P(50th toss will be a head)?

Q4 If the probability of picking a banana from a fruit bowl is 0.27, what is the probability of picking something which is not a banana?

Q5 A bag contains 3 red balls, 4 blue balls and 5 green balls. A ball is chosen at random from the bag. What is the probability that:
a) it is green
b) it is blue
c) it is red
d) it is not red?

Q6 Students at school conduct a survey of the colours of parents' cars, where every parent owns one car. The table shows the results.

Red	Blue	Yellow	White	Green	Other
40	29	13	20	16	14

a) What is the probability of a parent owning a red car?
b) What is the probability of a parent owning a car that is not blue or green?

Q7 The probability of it raining during the monsoon is ¾, on a particular day.
a) What is the probability of it not raining?
b) If a monsoon 'season' lasts approximately 100 days, how many days are likely to be dry?

Probability

Q8 Charlton is making a bet with his friend before the local cricket team play a match. He thinks the match will end in a draw. A local newspaper prints the team's results over their last 20 matches, as shown.

W	W	L	D	D	W	W	L	W	L
D	L	L	D	W	D	W	W	L	L

a) Complete the frequency table.

Outcome	Frequency
W	
D	
L	

b) Charlton reasons that since there are 3 possible results for any match, the probability that the next match will be drawn (D) is $\frac{1}{3}$. Explain why Charlton is wrong.

c) Suggest a value for the probability of a draw based on the team's past performance.

d) Based on their past performance, are the team most likely to win, lose, or draw?

Q9 **a)** What is the probability of randomly selecting either a black Ace or black King from an ordinary pack of playing cards?

Remember the OR rule — P(A or B) = P(A) + P(B).

b) If the entire suit of clubs is removed from a pack of cards, what is the probability of randomly selecting a red 7 from the remaining cards?

c) If all the 7s are also removed from the pack of cards, what is the probability of randomly selecting the 4 of diamonds?

Q10 For the roulette wheel shown, the probability of the ball landing on each of the numbers is listed in the table below.

Number	1	2	3	4	5	6
Probability	$\frac{1}{6}$	$\frac{1}{3}$	$\frac{1}{6}$	$\frac{1}{12}$	$\frac{1}{12}$	$\frac{1}{6}$

a) Find the probability of landing on an even number.

b) What is the probability of landing on black?

c) Why is the probability of landing on a white or a 3 not $\frac{5}{12} + \frac{1}{6}$?

Q11 The notepad below shows orders for 4 different sorts of rice at a certain Indian restaurant. Based on this data, what is the probability that the next order of rice is:

a) for pilau rice?

b) for spicy mushroom or special fried rice?

c) not for boiled rice?

boiled	20
pilau	24
spicy mushroom	10
special fried	6

If you're asked to work out probabilities based on some data, it's a relative frequency question.

Friday 11th October.

Probability

Q12 3 balls are drawn at random, without replacement, from a bag containing 4 green balls and 3 red balls.

a) Complete the tree diagram below showing all the possible outcomes and their probabilities.

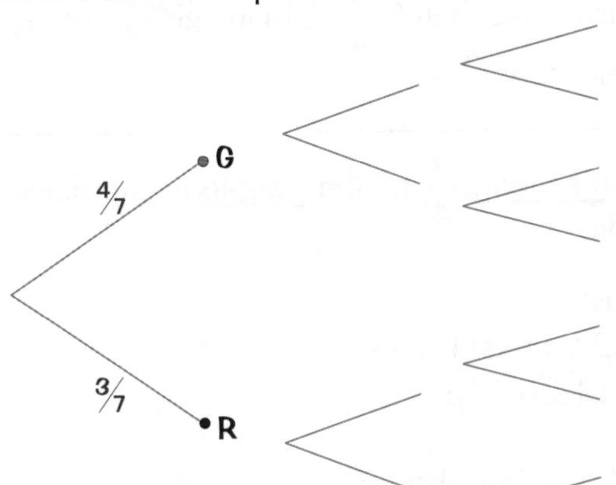

For AND you MULTIPLY along the branches. For OR you ADD the end results.

b) What is the probability that exactly 2 green balls are drawn?

c) What is the probability that the last ball drawn is the same colour as the first?

Q13 How many times must you roll an ordinary 6-sided dice for the probability of getting at least one 6 to be more than 0.5?

Don't forget the "at least" trick — P(at least 1 six) = 1 – P(no sixes).

Q14 3 coins are drawn at random, without replacement, from a piggy bank containing 7 pound coins and 4 twenty-pence pieces.

a) Draw a tree diagram showing all possible outcomes and their probabilities.

b) Find the probability that the first coin selected is different in value from the third.

c) Find the probability that less than £1.50 is drawn altogether.

Q15 Trevor and his 2 brothers and 5 friends are seated at random in a row of 8 seats at the cinema. What is the probability that Trevor has one brother on his immediate left and one on his immediate right?

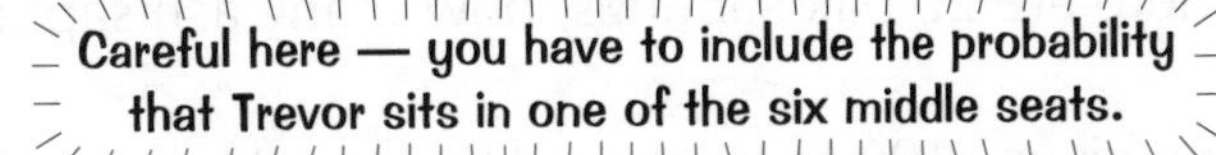

Careful here — you have to include the probability that Trevor sits in one of the six middle seats.

Drawing a tree diagram might be a bit of a faff, but it can really help to make the question clearer. So if you're stuck, give the old tree diagram a try.

Ratios

I don't want to spoil the surprise, but you're going to need your calculator for this bit — get your finger on that fraction button...

Turn RATIOS into FRACTIONS

If girls and boys are in the ratio 3:4, this means there's $\frac{3}{4}$ as many girls as boys.
So if there were 20 boys, there would be $\frac{3}{4} \times 20 = 15$ girls.

You've got to be careful though — it doesn't mean $\frac{3}{4}$ of the people in the class are girls. In fact, three sevenths of the class are girls.

Q1 Write these ratios in their simplest forms:

a) 6:8 **c)** 1.5:3 **e)** 2 weeks:4 days
b) 5:20 **d)** 2¼:4 **f)** £1.26:14p

Q2 A rectangle has sides in the ratio 1:2. Calculate the length of the longer side if the shorter side is:

a) 3 cm **b)** 5.5 cm **c)** 15.2 m

Calculate the length of the shorter side if the longer side is:

d) 3 cm **e)** 5.5 cm **f)** 15.2 m

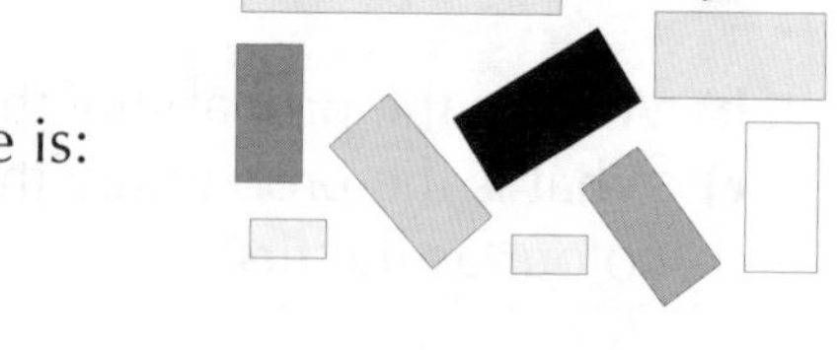

Q3 Divide the following amounts in the ratios given:

a) £20 in the ratio 2:3 **c)** 500 g in the ratio 1:2:2
b) 150 m in the ratio 8:7 **d)** 8 hrs in the ratio 1:2:3

For these you add up the ratio numbers to find the total number of parts and divide by this. Then multiply by each number in the ratio separately to find the different amounts.

Q4 a) Increase £3.20 in the ratio 2:3.
b) Decrease 120 cm in the ratio 3:2.

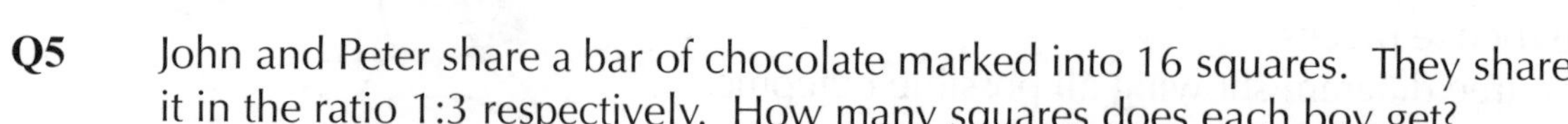

Q5 John and Peter share a bar of chocolate marked into 16 squares. They share it in the ratio 1:3 respectively. How many squares does each boy get?

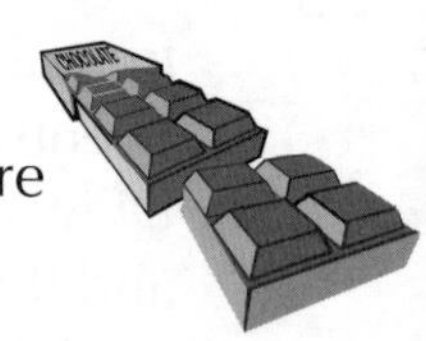

Q6 A 2 litre bottle of cola is to be shared between three girls in the ratio 2:3:5. How many millilitres will each girl get?

Watch out for your units — you'll have to change them over for this one — and your answer should be in millilitres.

Q7 Oak and ash saplings are planted along a roadside in the ratio 2:3 respectively. If there are 20 oak saplings, how many ash saplings are there?

Q8 Tony gives £100 to be shared by Jane, Holly and Rosemary in a ratio according to their age. Jane is 10, Holly is 12 and Rosemary is 3 years old. How much will each child get?

Q9 Sunil and Paul work in a restaurant. As they work different hours, they split their tips in the ratio 3:4. One night they got £28 in tips between them. Who got the most money from the tips and how much did they get?

Ratios

Q10 The recipe for flapjacks is 250 g of oats, 150 g of brown sugar and 100 g of margarine. What fraction of the mixture is:

a) oats?
b) sugar?

Q11 The ratio of girls to boys in a school is 7:6. If there are 455 pupils in total, how many are

a) girls?
b) boys?

Q12 Sarah works as a waitress. Each week, she splits her wage into spending money and savings in the ratio 7:3.

a) One week, Sarah earns £130. How much should she put in her savings that week?
b) The next week, Sarah put £42 into her savings. How much did she earn in total that week?

Q13 An architect is drawing the plan of a house to a scale of 1 cm to 3 m.

a) Write this ratio in its simplest form.
b) How wide is a room that appears as 2 cm on the drawing?
c) The hall is 10 m long. How long will the architect need to make it on the drawing?

Make sure you convert to the same units when you're working out the ratio.

Q14 Concrete is mixed using cement, sand and gravel in the ratio 1:3:6. If Dave uses a 5 kg bag of cement, how much:

a) sand does he need?
b) gravel does he need?
c) If Dave needs 80 kg of concrete, how much of each substance does he need?

Q15

I picked some strawberries after a few wet days. Some were nibbled by snails, some were mouldy and some fine. The ratio was 2:3:10 respectively. If 9 strawberries were mouldy how many:

a) were fine?
b) were not fine?
c) What fraction of the total amount were fine?

Q16 Salt & Vinegar, Cheese & Onion and Prawn Cocktail flavour crisps were sold in the school tuck shop in the ratio 5:3:2. If 18 bags of Prawn Cocktail were sold, how many bags:

a) of Salt & Vinegar were sold?
b) were sold altogether?

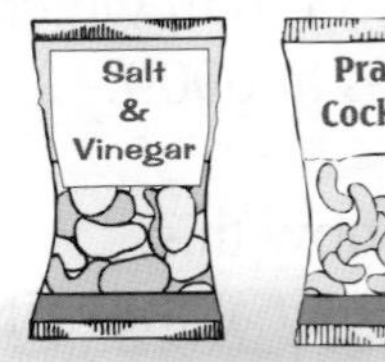

Travel Graphs

You need to remember what the different bits of a travel graph mean — what it looks like when <u>stopped</u>, <u>changing speed</u> and <u>coming back</u> to the starting point.

Q1 Peter set out from A at 0900 to walk to B.

a) How far did he walk in the 1st hour?

b) He stopped twice; how long was each stop?

c) What was his speed after the second stop?

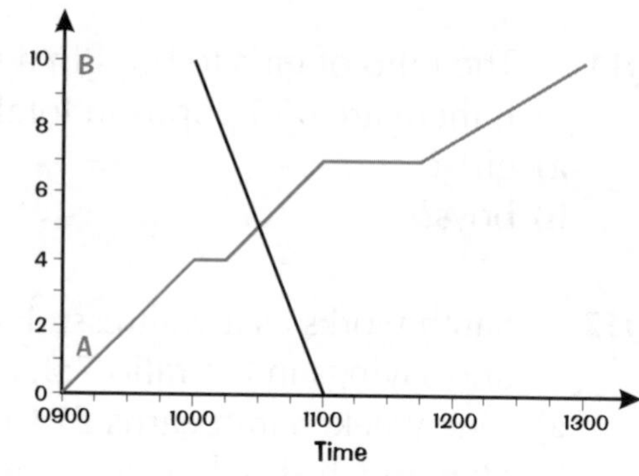

At 1000 Sarah set out on her bike to ride from B to A.

d) What time did she arrive at A?

e) What was her average speed?

f) At what time did Peter and Sarah pass each other?

Q2 Dave drives a bus from Kendal to Ingleton and back again. The bus company graphed the journey to help them organise their bus schedules.

a) How long did it take to get to Ingleton?

b) How much time was spent driving to and from Ingleton excluding stops?

c) What was the average speed for the journey from Kendal to Ingleton?

d) What was Dave's fastest speed?

e) The transport manager wants Dave to reduce the duration of the stops on the Kendal to Ingleton route so that he can make another journey from Kendal to Windermere starting at 1630. Would this be possible?

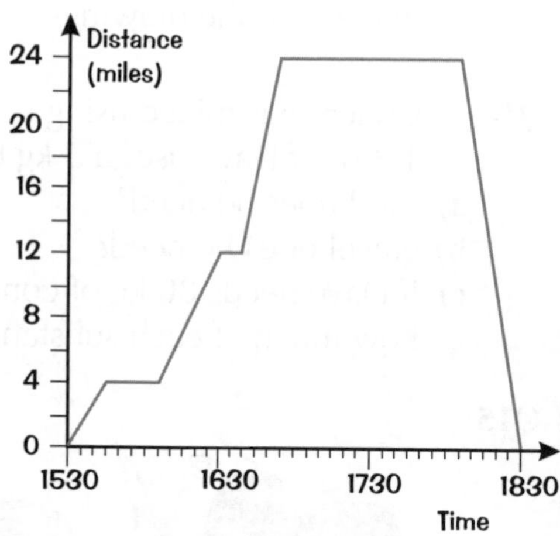

Q3 Mr. Smith leaves home at 0730 to go to work. He walks at a steady 6 km/h for 2 km. He catches the 0755 train which takes 35 mins to travel 50 km. He then walks 3 km to work and arrives at 0900.

Draw a graph to show this.
How long did he wait at the station for the train?

Travel Graphs

Q4 A train operator plans to purchase a new engine. They've graphed the journeys made by five engines over a 100 km stretch of track to help them decide which one is best.

a) Calculate the speed of each train and state which one was the fastest.

b) How could you tell by looking at the diagram which was the fastest and which was the slowest?

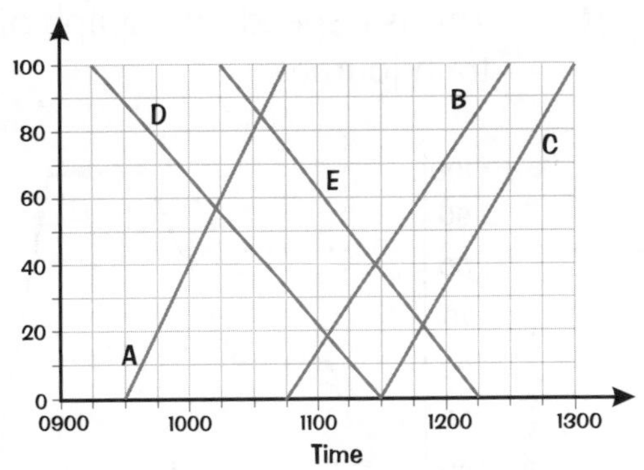

Q5 On sports day the first three in the 1000 m race ran as shown in the graph below.

a) Which runner, A, B or C, won the race?

b) How long did the winner take?

c) Which runner kept up a steady speed?

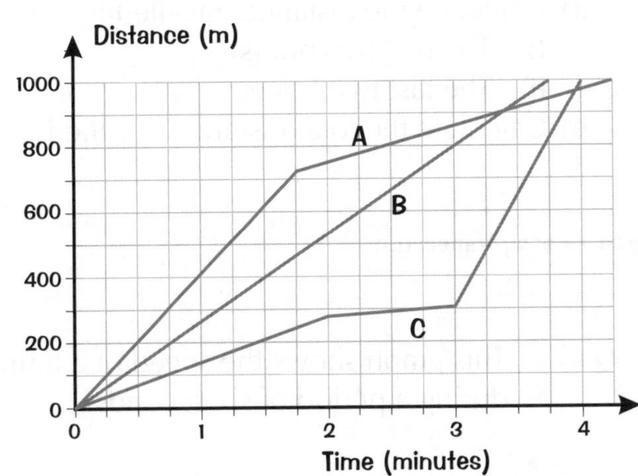

d) What was that speed

i) in m/min?

ii) km/h?

e) Which runner achieved the fastest speed and what was that speed?

Q6 Two cars start a journey at midday (1200) — one travels from town A to village B, and the other from village B to town A. A and B are 80 km apart. The car from town A travels at an average speed of 48 km/h and the other car, from village B, at 60 km/h.

a) Draw a graph to show these journeys.

b) At what time do the cars pass? (approx.)

c) How far from A are they when they pass?

Use the speeds given to work out the time it takes for each car to travel the 80 km.

Q7 A girl set off on an all-day walk. She started at 0915 and walked at a steady speed for 9 km before stopping at 1100 for a 20 min break. She then set off again at a steady speed and walked 8 km, stopping at 1300 for 45 mins. After lunch she walked at $3\frac{1}{2}$ km/h for $2\frac{1}{2}$ hrs to her destination.

a) Draw a graph to show this walk.

b) How far did she walk altogether?

c) What was the average speed for the whole walk?

d) What was her fastest walking speed?

Areas and Gradients of Graphs

Q1 This is a speed-time graph of a train journey.

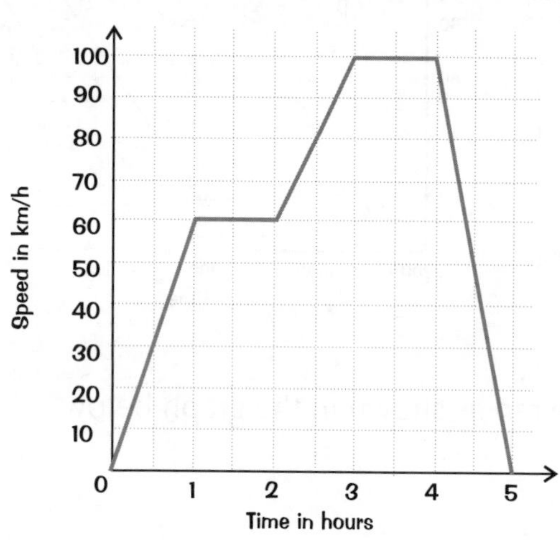

a) Calculate the distance travelled in:

i) The first two hours.

ii) The last two hours.

b) Calculate the total distance travelled.

Q2 Andrew's cycle computer plots a graph of his journey but only shows his speed.

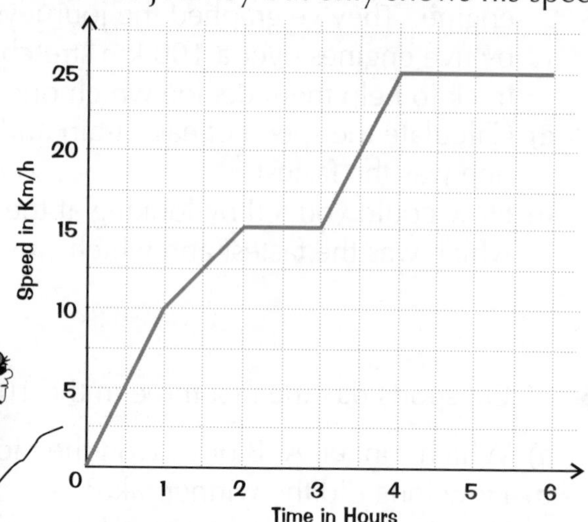

He wants to know how far he travelled.

a) Calculate the distance travelled in:

i) The first two hours.

ii) The last two hours.

b) Calculate the total distance travelled.

Add up all the little trapezia to find the whole area — easy trapeasy...

Q3 This graph shows the speed of a train during a period of eight seconds.

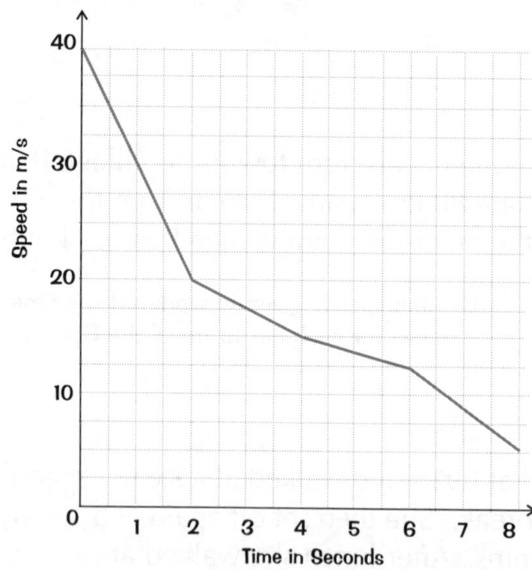

a) Estimate the total distance travelled in this period by dividing the area into four trapeziums of equal width.

b) Estimate the train's deceleration during the first 2 seconds.

Q4 This graph shows the speed of a train during a period of six seconds.

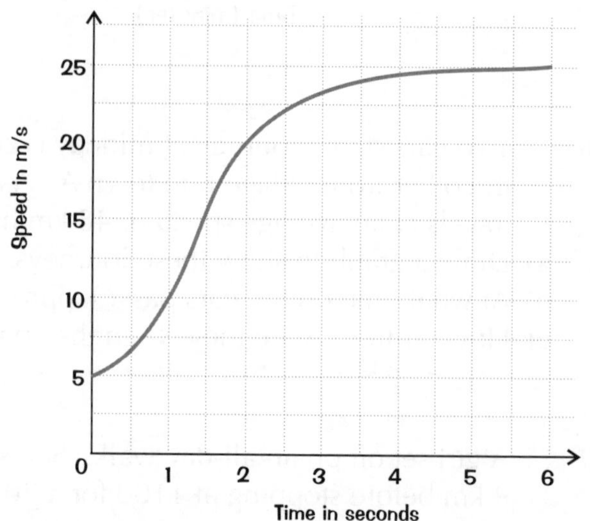

a) Estimate the total distance travelled in the period of six seconds by dividing the area into four trapeziums.

b) Estimate the train's acceleration at 2 seconds by drawing a tangent to the curve.

Direct and Inverse Proportion

Q1 If 17 textbooks cost £150.45, how much will 28 cost?

Q2 If it takes 4 people 28 hours to complete a task, how long would it take just one person?

Q3 On a map, 2 cm represents 3 km.

a) If two towns are 14 km apart, what is the distance between them on the map?

b) If two road junctions are 20.3 cm apart on the map, what is their real distance apart?

Q4 y is directly proportional to x. If $y = 5$ when x is 25, find y when x is 100.

Q5 Complete the following tables of values where y is always directly proportional to x.

a)

x	2	4	6
y	5	10	

b)

x	3	6	9
y		9	

c)

x	27		
y	5	10	15

Q6 If $y \propto \frac{1}{x}$ and $x = 4$ when $y = 5$, find the value of x when $y = 10$.

Q7 Given that $y \propto \frac{1}{x}$, complete this table of values.

x	1	2	3	4	5	6
y					9.6	

Put the numbers into the equation y = k/x to find the value of k. Then you can find the rest of the ys.

Q8 Two cylindrical containers are filled to the same depth, d cm, with water. The mass of the water in each container is proportional to the square of the radius of each container. The first container has a radius of 16 cm and the water has a mass of 16 kg. If the second container has a radius of 8 cm, find the mass of the water inside it.

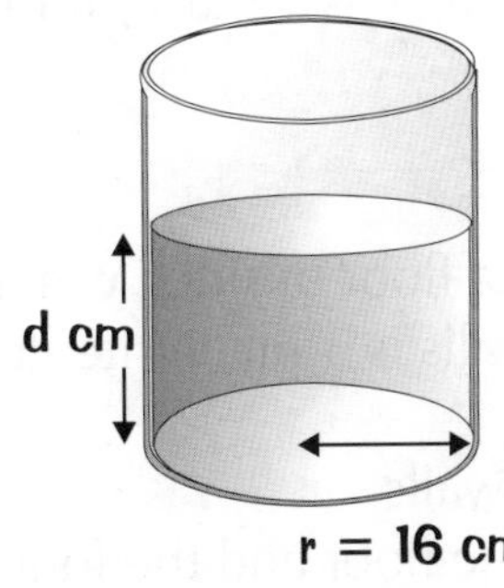

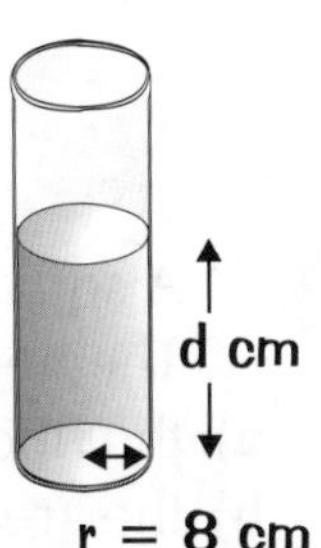

Factorising Quadratics

Q1 Factorise the quadratics first, and then solve the equations:

a) $x^2 + 3x - 10 = 0$
b) $x^2 - 5x + 6 = 0$
c) $x^2 - 2x + 1 = 0$
d) $x^2 - 4x + 3 = 0$
e) $x^2 - x - 20 = 0$
f) $x^2 - 4x - 5 = 0$
g) $x^2 + 6x - 7 = 0$
h) $x^2 + 14x + 49 = 0$
i) $x^2 - 2x - 15 = 0$.

Q2 Rearrange into the form "$x^2 + bx + c = 0$", then solve by factorising:

a) $x^2 + 6x = 16$
b) $x^2 + 5x = 36$
c) $x^2 + 4x = 45$
d) $x^2 = 5x$
e) $x^2 = 11x$
f) $x^2 - 21 = 4x$
g) $x^2 - 300 = 20x$
h) $x^2 + 48 = 26x$
i) $x^2 + 36 = 13x$
j) $x + 5 - \frac{14}{x} = 0$
k) $x + 4 - \frac{21}{x} = 0$
l) $x(x - 3) = 10$
m) $x^2 - 3(x + 6) = 0$
n) $x - \frac{63}{x} = 2$
o) $x + 1 = \frac{12}{x}$

Q3 Solve $x^2 - \frac{1}{4} = 0$.

Q4 The area of a rectangular swimming pool is 28 m^2. The width is x m. The difference between the length and width is 3 m. Find the value of x.

Q5 A rug has length x m. The width is exactly 1 m less than the length.

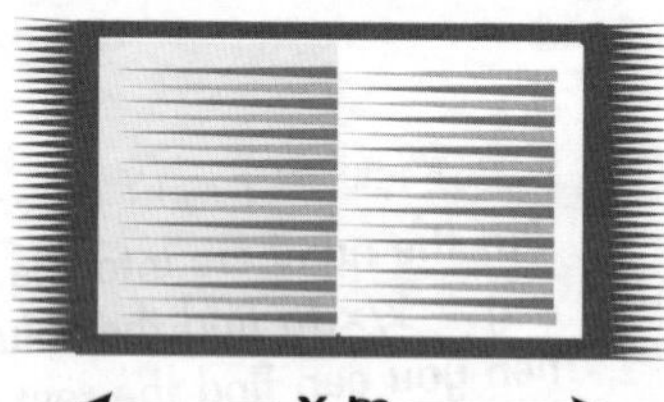

a) Write down an expression for the area of the rug.
b) If the area of the rug is 6 m^2, find the value of x.

Q6 A triangle has height $(x + 1)$ cm and a base of $2x$ cm.
a) Write down an expression for the area of the triangle and simplify it.
b) If the area of the triangle is 12 cm^2, find the value of x.

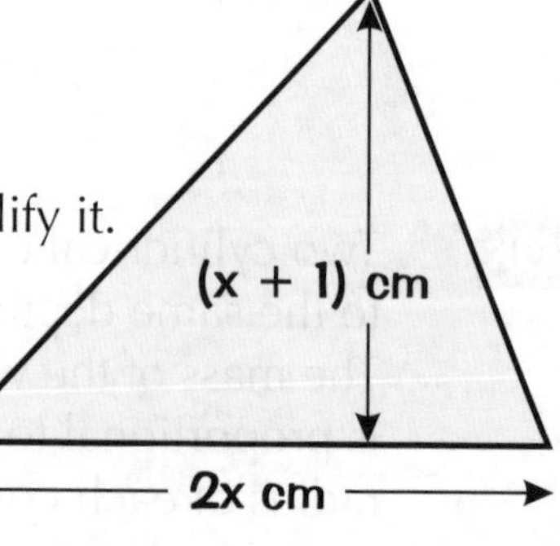

Q7 A square room has a floor of sides x metres.
The height of the walls is 3 m. Write down an expression for:
a) the floor area
b) the area of all four walls.
c) If the total area of the floor and the four walls is 64 m^2, form a quadratic equation and solve it to find x.

The Quadratic Formula

Q1 Find the two values, to 2 d.p, given by each of the following expressions:

a) $\frac{2 \pm \sqrt{3}}{2}$

b) $\frac{4 \pm \sqrt{10}}{3}$

c) $\frac{-2 \pm \sqrt{27}}{2}$

d) $\frac{-3 \pm \sqrt{42}}{3}$

e) $\frac{-10 \pm \sqrt{160}}{5}$

f) $\frac{-27 \pm \sqrt{10}}{2}$

g) $\frac{-8 \pm \sqrt{9.5}}{2.4}$

h) $\frac{10 \pm \sqrt{88.4}}{23.2}$

Q2 The following quadratics can be solved by factorisation, but practise using the formula to solve them.

a) $x^2 + 8x + 12 = 0$
b) $6x^2 - x - 2 = 0$
c) $x^2 - x - 6 = 0$
d) $x^2 - 3x + 2 = 0$
e) $4x^2 - 15x + 9 = 0$
f) $x^2 - 3x = 0$
g) $36x^2 - 48x + 16 = 0$
h) $3x^2 + 8x = 0$
i) $2x^2 - 7x - 4 = 0$
j) $x^2 + x - 20 = 0$
k) $4x^2 + 8x - 12 = 0$
l) $3x^2 - 11x - 20 = 0$
m) $x + 3 = 2x^2$
n) $5 - 3x - 2x^2 = 0$
o) $1 - 5x + 6x^2 = 0$
p) $3(x^2 + 2x) = 9$
q) $x^2 + 4(x - 3) = 0$
r) $x^2 = 2(4 - x)$

Step number 1... Write out the formula.

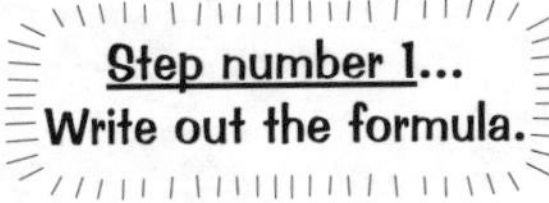

Step number 2...
Write down values
for a, b and c.

Step number 3... sub a, b and c into the formula. Make sure you divide the whole of the top line by 2a — not just ½ of it.

Q3 Solve the following quadratics using the formula. Give your answers to no more than two decimal places.

a) $x^2 + 3x - 1 = 0$
b) $x^2 - 2x - 6 = 0$
c) $x^2 + x - 1 = 0$
d) $x^2 + 6x + 3 = 0$
e) $x^2 + 5x + 2 = 0$
f) $x^2 - x - 1 = 0$
g) $3x^2 + 10x - 8 = 0$
h) $x^2 + 4x + 2 = 0$
i) $x^2 - 6x - 8 = 0$
j) $x^2 - 14x + 11 = 0$
k) $x^2 + 3x - 5 = 0$
l) $7x^2 - 15x + 6 = 0$
m) $2x^2 + 6x - 3 = 0$
n) $2x^2 - 7x + 4 = 0$

Oops, forgot to mention step number 4... check your answers by putting them back in the equation.

The Quadratic Formula

Q4 Rearrange the following in the form "$ax^2 + bx + c = 0$" and then solve by the quadratic formula. Give your answers to two decimal places.

a) $x^2 = 8 - 3x$

b) $(x + 2)^2 - 3 = 0$

c) $3x(x - 1) = 5$

d) $2x(x + 4) = 1$

e) $x^2 = 4(x + 1)$

f) $(2x - 1)^2 = 5$

g) $3x^2 + 2x = 6$

h) $(x + 2)(x + 3) = 5$

i) $(x - 2)(2x - 1) = 3$

j) $2x + \frac{4}{x} = 7$

k) $\left(x - \frac{1}{2}\right)^2 = \frac{1}{4}$

l) $4x(x - 2) = -3$

Q5 The sides of the triangle ABC are as shown. Given that $(AB)^2 = (AC)^2 + (BC)^2$, form a quadratic equation in x and then solve it to find x.

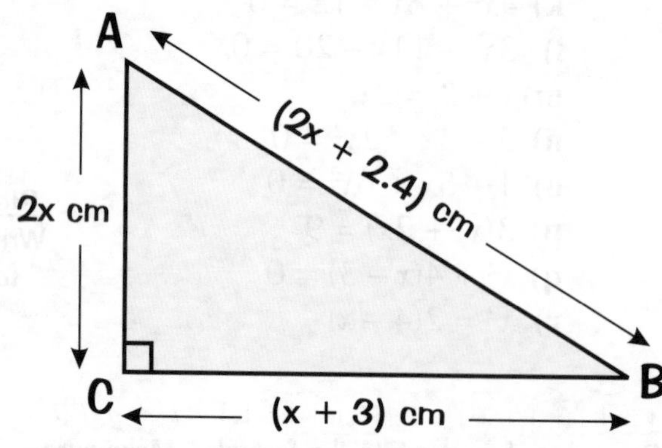

Q6 The area of a rectangle with length $(x + 4.6)$ cm and width $(x - 2.1)$ cm is 134.63 cm^2.

a) Form a quadratic equation and solve it to find x to two decimal places.

b) What is the rectangle's perimeter to one decimal place?

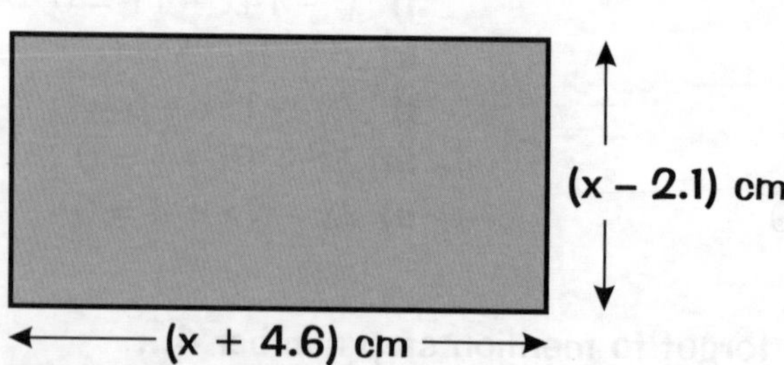

Quadratic Equations and Graphs

Q1 The diagram shows the graphs:
$y = x^2 - x$
$y = x + 2$
$y = 8$
$y = -2x + 4$

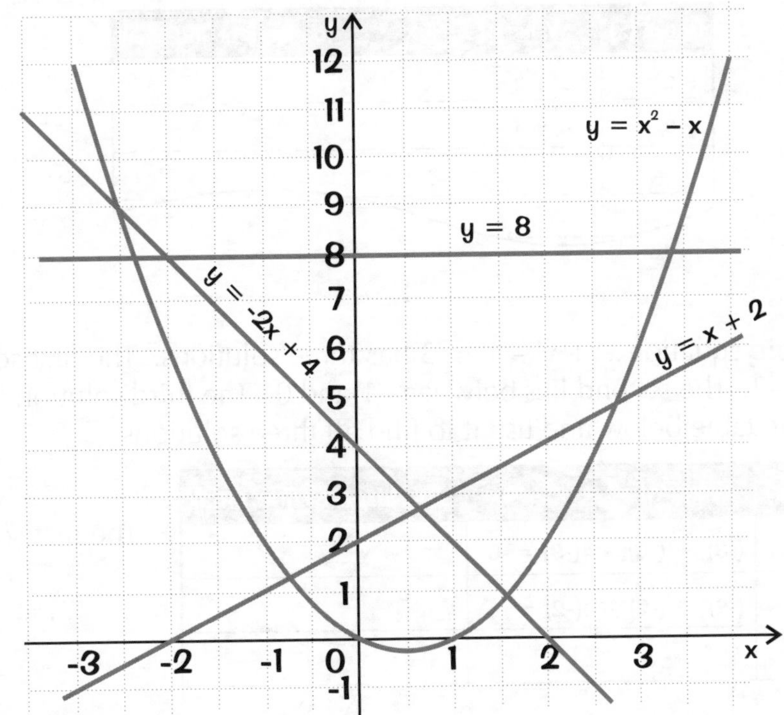

Use the graphs to find the solutions to:

a) $x^2 - x = 0$

b) $x^2 - x = x + 2$

c) $x^2 - x = 8$

d) $x^2 - x = -2x + 4$

e) $x^2 - x - 8 = 0$

f) $x^2 + x = 4$

These equations look a bit nasty, but they're just made up of the equations you've got graphs for. And you know how to do the rest of it, don't you...

Q2 Complete this table for $y = -\frac{1}{2}x^2 + 5$:

x	-4	-3	-2	-1	0	1	2	3	4
$-\frac{1}{2}x^2$									
+5									
y									

Draw the graph $y = -\frac{1}{2}x^2 + 5$.
Use your graph to solve the following equations (to 1 d.p.):

a) $-\frac{1}{2}x^2 + 5 = 0$ **b)** $-\frac{1}{2}x^2 + 5 = -3$ **c)** $-\frac{1}{2}x^2 + 5 = x$

Trial and Improvement

Q1 The cubic equation $x^3 + x = 24$ has a solution between 2 and 3. Copy the table below and use it to find this solution to 1 d.p.

Guess (x)	Value of $x^3 + x$	Too large or Too small
2	$2^3 + 2 =$	
3	$3^3 + 3 =$	

Q2 The cubic equation $x^3 + x^2 - 4x = 3$ has three solutions. The first solution lies between −3 and −2. The second lies between −1 and 0. The third solution lies between 1 and 2. Copy the table below and use it to find all three solutions.

Guess (x)	Value of $x^3 + x^2 - 4x$	Too large or Too small
−3	$(-3)^3 + (-3)^2 - 4(-3) = -6$	
−2	$(-2)^3 + (-2)^2 - 4(-2) =$	
⋮	⋮	⋮
−1	$(-1)^3 + (-1)^2 - 4(-1) =$	
0	$(0)^3 + (0)^2 - 4(0) =$	
⋮	⋮	⋮
1	$(1)^3 + (1)^2 - 4(1) =$	
2	$(2)^3 + (2)^2 - 4(2) =$	

The first solution is

.... to 1d.p.

The second solution is

.... to 1d.p.

The third solution is

.... to 1d.p.

Q3 For a craft project, Steph is making some simple boxes. She cuts out squares of side length x cm from square pieces of card measuring 20 cm by 20 cm, then folds up the sides, as shown. The volume of the boxes (V) can be calculated using the cubic equation:

$$4x^3 - 80x^2 + 400x = V.$$

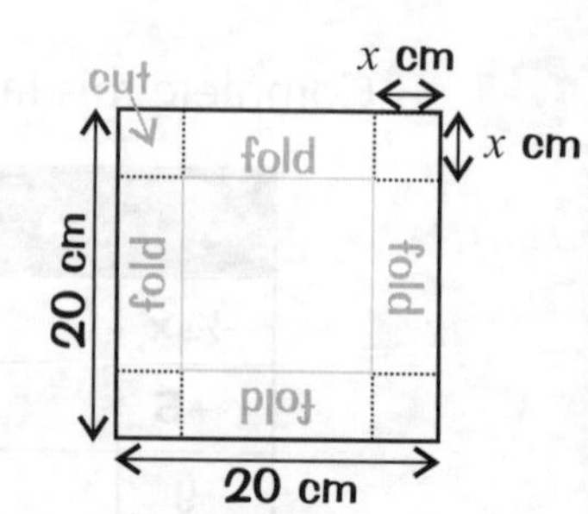

Use trial and improvement to find the value of x she must use to give the biggest volume of box possible, giving the answer to 1 d.p. The solution lies between 3 cm and 4 cm.

They don't always give you the starting numbers — so if they don't, make sure you pick two opposite cases (one too big, one too small), or you've blown it.

Polygons

The one thing they're guaranteed to ask you about is Interior and Exterior Angles — you'd better get learning those formulas...

A POLYGON is a many-sided shape. A REGULAR polygon is one where ALL THE SIDES AND ANGLES ARE THE SAME.

You need to know these two formulas:

1) EXTERIOR ANGLE = 360° ÷ No. of Sides

2) INTERIOR ANGLE = 180° – EXTERIOR ANGLE

Q1 What sort of triangles occur in every regular polygon (except a hexagon), when each vertex is joined to the centre by a straight line?

Q2 A square and a regular hexagon are placed adjacent to each other.

a) What is the size of ∠PQW?

b) What is the size of ∠PRW?

c) How many sides has the regular polygon that has ∠PQW as one of its angles?

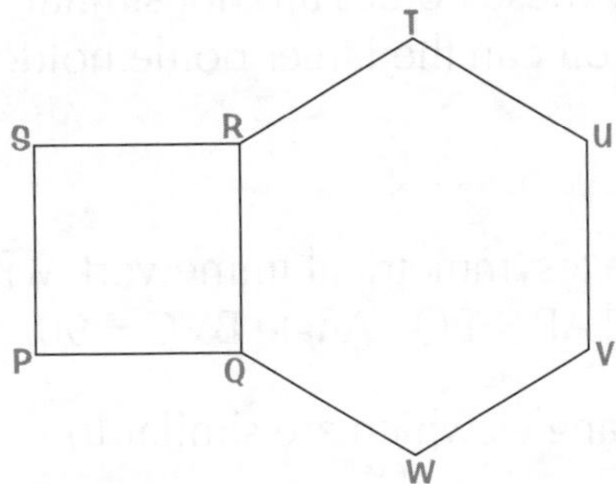

Q3 An irregular pentagon has interior angles of 100°, 104°, 120°. If the other two angles are equal, what is their size?

Q4 a) The sum of the interior angles of a regular 24-sided polygon is 3960°. Use this to calculate the size of one interior angle.

b) From your answer to part **a)** calculate one exterior angle and show that the sum of the exterior angles equals 360°.

Q5

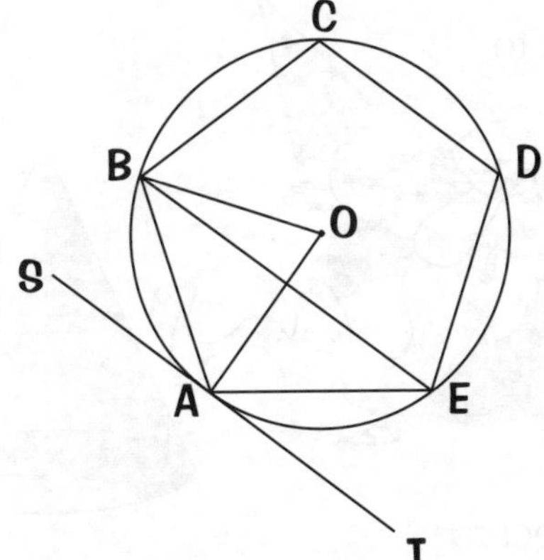

ABCDE is a regular pentagon. It is drawn in a circle centre O. SAT is a tangent drawn to the circle at A.

a) Calculate the size of angle BOA.

b) Find the size of angle OBA.

c) Write down the size of angle:

i) SAO

ii) BAS.

d) Hence write down the size of angle BEA giving a reason for your answer.

Q6 The sum of the interior angles of a regular polygon is 2520°. How many sides does this regular polygon have?

Remember that formula for the sum of interior angles — it comes in handy here.

Similarity

Q1 In the diagram below, BC is parallel to DE.
AB = 12 cm, BD = 8 cm, DE = 25 cm and CE = 10 cm.

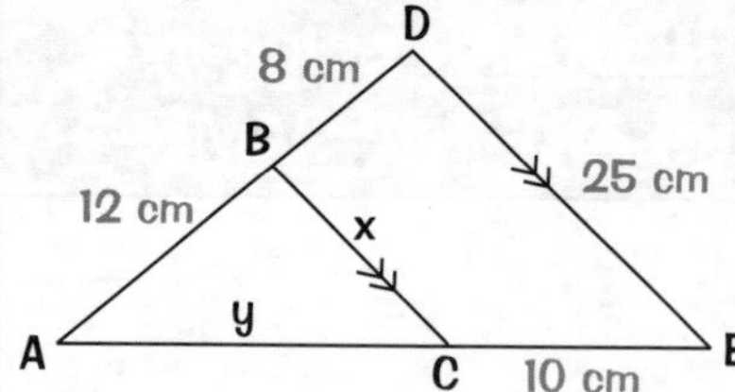

a) Explain why triangles ABC and ADE are similar.
b) Find the lengths of x and y in the diagram.

Q2 A cylindrical bottle can hold 1 litre of oil. A second cylindrical bottle has twice the radius but the same height. It also contains oil.
a) Explain why these bottles are not similar.
b) How much oil can the larger bottle hold?

Q3 A boy made a symmetrical framework with metal rods as shown. Lengths AB = BC, ST = TC and AP = PQ. Angle BVC = 90° and length BV = 9 cm.

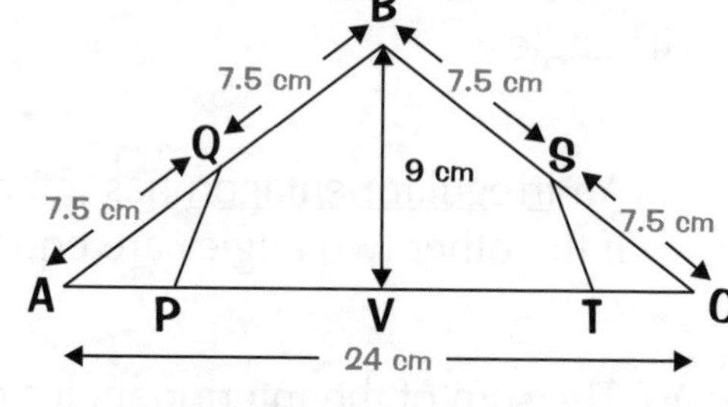

a) Find two triangles which are similar to triangle ABC.
b) Calculate the length of AP. Hence write down the length of PT.
c) Calculate the area of triangle ABC.
d) Find the area of triangle APQ. Give your answer correct to 3 significant figures.
e) Hence write down the area of PQBST correct to 2 significant figures.

Q4 On a holiday near the sea, children built a sandcastle in the shape of a cone. The radius of the base is 100 cm and the height is 100 cm.
a) What is the volume of the sandcastle in m³ correct to 3 significant figures?
The children now remove the top portion to make a similar cone but only 50 cm in height.

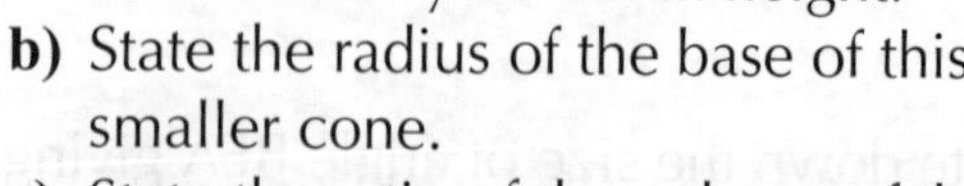

b) State the radius of the base of this smaller cone.
c) State the ratio of the volume of the small cone to the volume of the original cone.
d) Calculate the volume of the small cone in m³ correct to 3 significant figures.
e) Hence write down the ratio of the volume of the portion left of the original cone to the smaller cone in the form n:1.

Pythagoras' Theorem

Don't try and do it all in your head — you've got to label the sides or you're bound to mess it up. Go on, get your pen out...

Q1 Find the length of the hypotenuse in each of the following triangles.

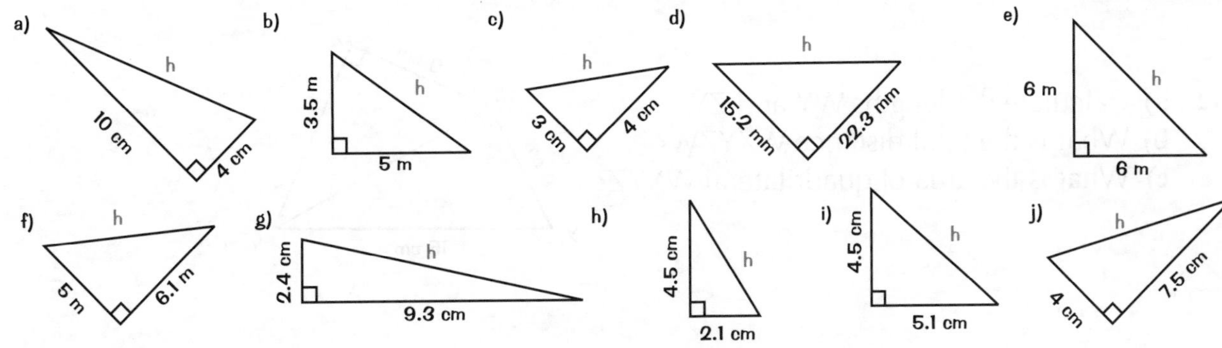

Q2 Find the length of the shorter side in each of the following triangles.

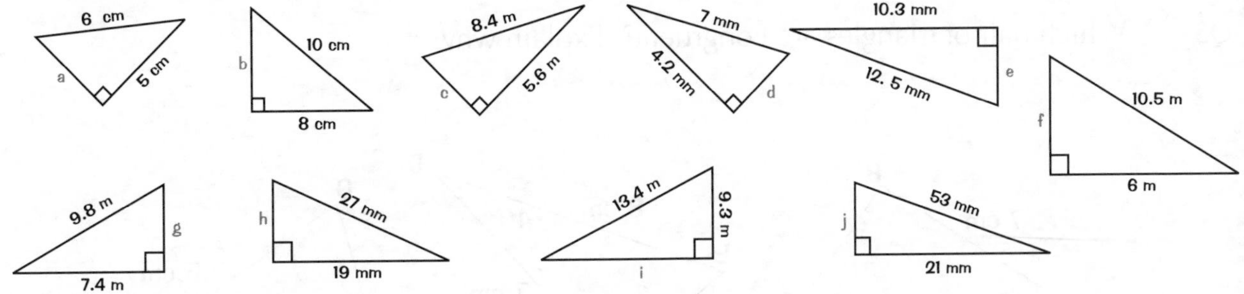

Q3 Find the unknown length in each of the following triangles.

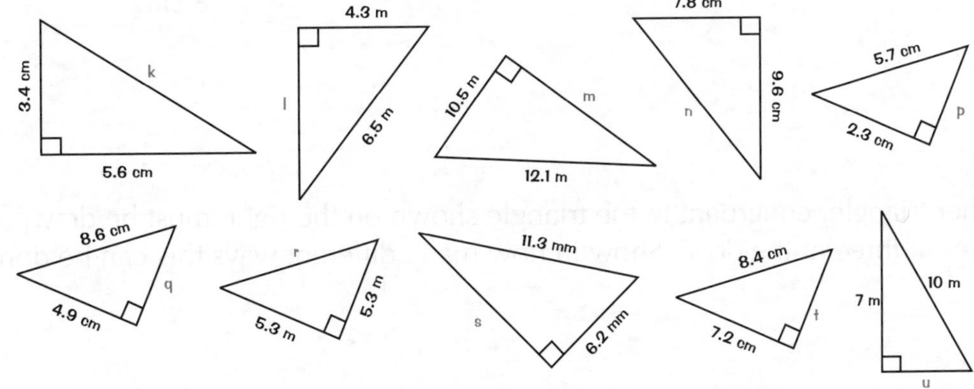

Q4 A window cleaner wants to clean the upstairs windows of an office. To meet safety regulations, his 10 m long ladder needs to be angled so that the bottom of the ladder is at least 2.6 m away from the wall. What is the maximum height that the top of the ladder can reach when used safely? Give your answer to 1 decimal place.

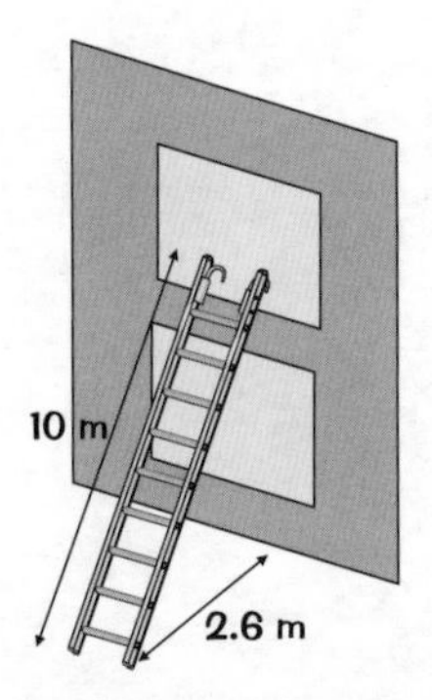

Pythagoras' Theorem and Congruence

Q1 A rectangular field is 250 m by 190 m. How far is it across diagonally?

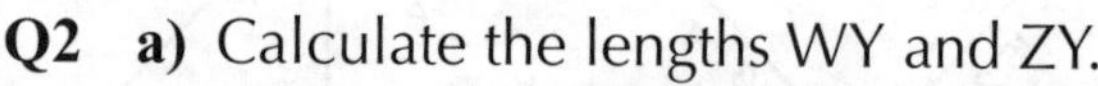

Q2 **a)** Calculate the lengths WY and ZY.
b) What is the total distance WXYZW?
c) What is the area of quadrilateral WXYZ?

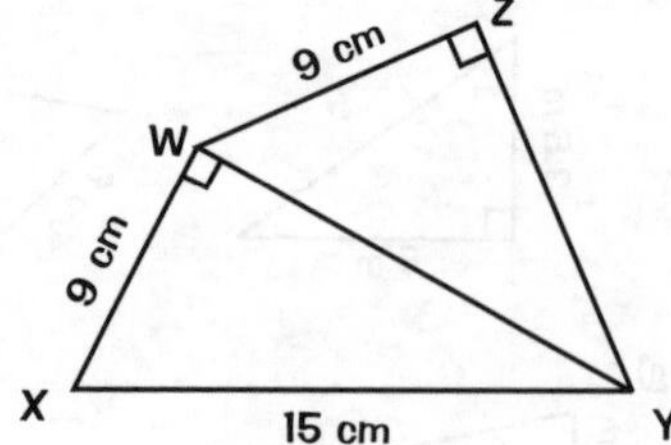

Q3 Which pair of triangles are congruent? Explain why.

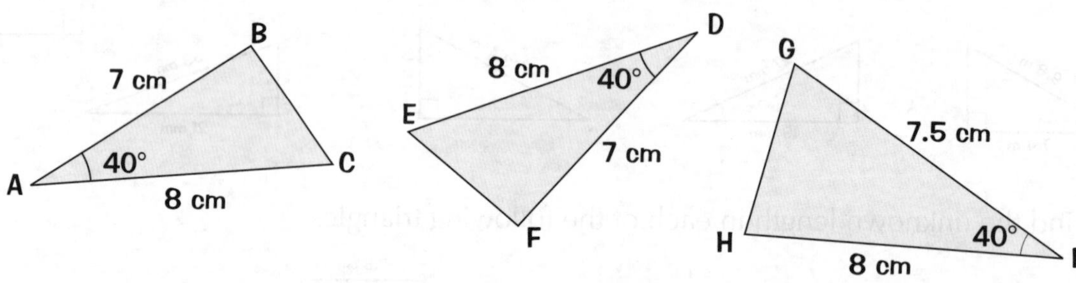

Q4 Another triangle, congruent to the triangle shown on the right, must be drawn with vertices at three of the dots. Show in how many different ways this can be done.

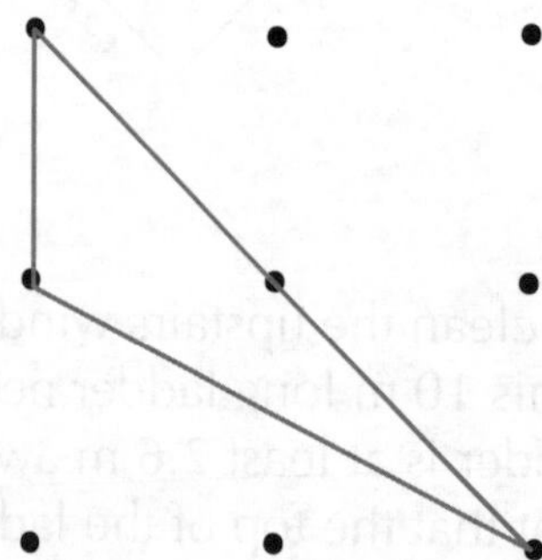

Trigonometry

Before you start a trigonometry question, write down the ratios, using SOH CAH TOA (Sockatoa!) — it'll help you pick your formula.

Q1 Calculate the tan, sin and cos of each of these angles:
a) 17° **b)** 83° **c)** 5° **d)** 28° **e)** 45°.

Q2 Use the tangent ratio to find the unknowns:

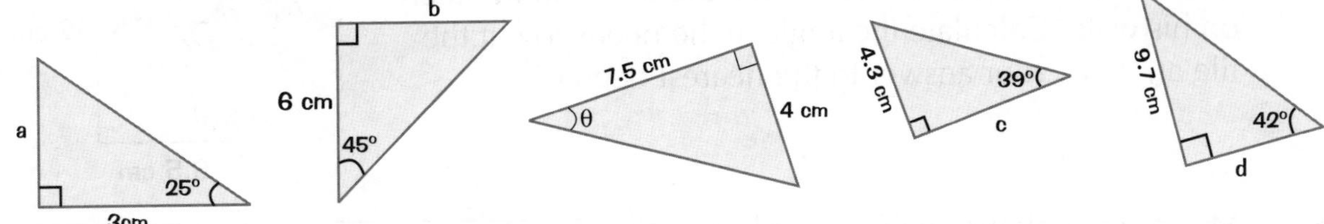

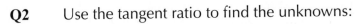

Q3 Use the cosine ratio to find the unknowns:

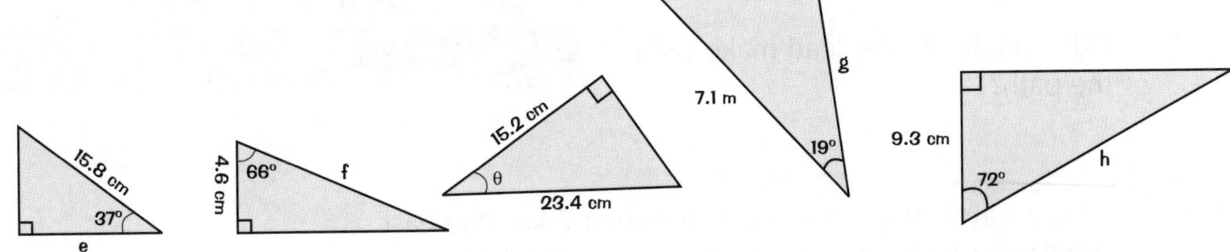

Q4 Use the sine ratio to find the unknowns:

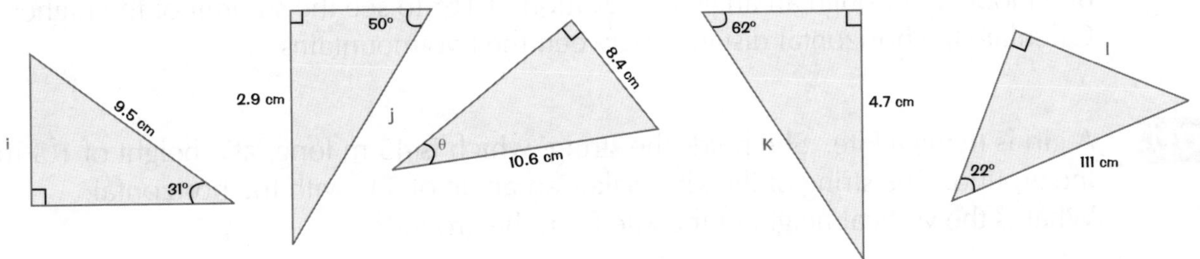

Q5 Find the unknowns using the appropriate ratios:

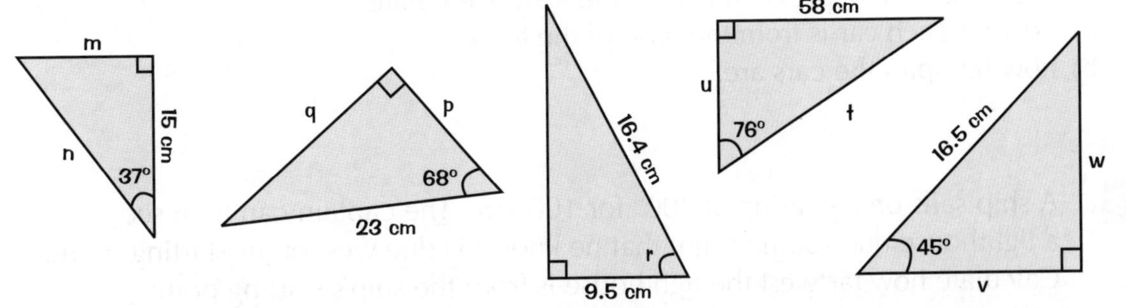

Trigonometry

Q6 A right-angled triangle has sides measuring 30 m, 40 m and 50 m.

a) Draw a rough sketch of the triangle, clearly labelling the hypotenuse.

b) Calculate the size of the smallest angle.

Make sure you've got the hang of the inverse SIN, COS and TAN functions on your calc... and check it's in DEG mode or you'll get nowhere fast.

Q7 Geoff is tiling his bathroom. He needs to cut off the right-angled triangle shown so that the tiles will fit nicely on his wall. Calculate the angle, θ, he needs to cut the tile at. Give your answer to the nearest degree.

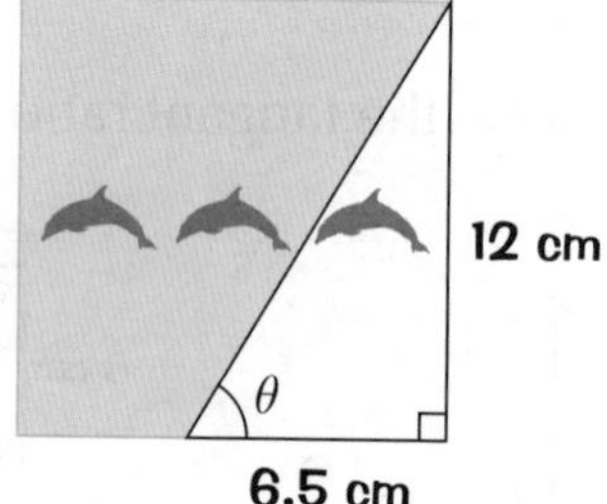

Q8 Mr Brown took his dog for a walk in the park. The dog's lead was 2 m long. The dog ran 0.7 m from the path Mr Brown was walking on.

What angle did the lead make with the path?

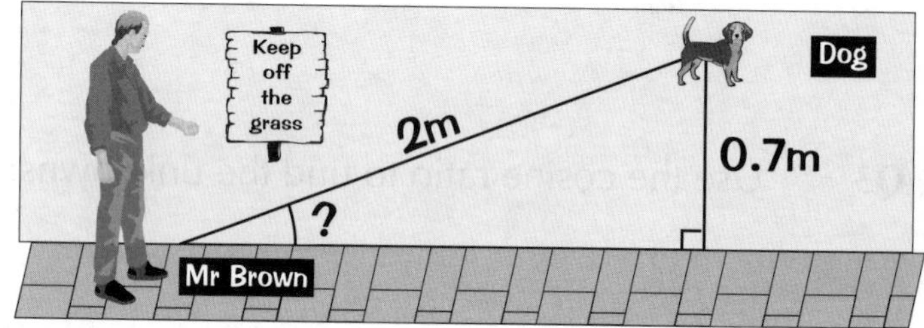

Q9 A boat travels 9 km due south and then 7 km due east. What bearing must it travel on to return to base?

Q10 Two mountains are 1020 m and 1235 m high. Standing on the summit of the lower one I look up through an angle of elevation of 16° to see the summit of the higher one. Calculate the horizontal distance between the two mountains.

Q11 A girl is flying a kite. She holds the string, which is 45 m long, at a height of 1.3 m above the ground. The string of the kite makes an angle of 33° with the horizontal. What is the vertical height of the kite from the ground?

Q12 I am standing on top of an 80 m high tower. I look due north and see two cars with angles of depression of 38° and 49°. Calculate:

a) how far each car is from the base of the tower

b) how far apart the cars are.

Q13 A ship sails on a bearing of 300° for 100 km. The captain can then see a lighthouse due south of him that he knows is due west of his starting point. Calculate how far west the lighthouse is from the ship's starting point.

3D Pythagoras and Trigonometry

Q1

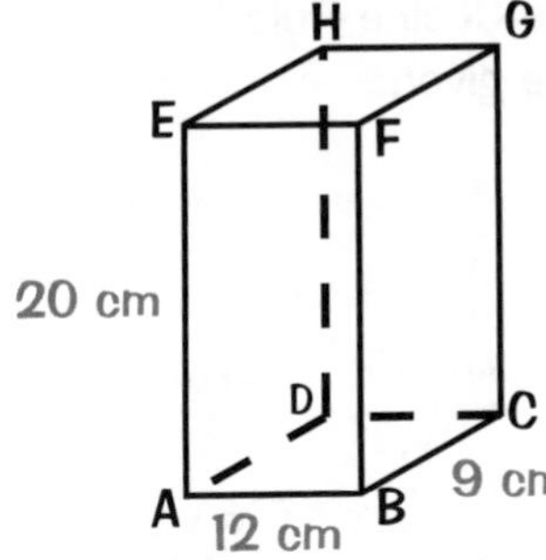

This rectangular box is 20 cm by 12 cm by 9 cm. Calculate:

a) angle ABE
b) length AF
c) length DF
d) angle EBH.

Q2 This pyramid is on a square base of side 56 cm. Its vertical height is 32 cm. Calculate the length of:

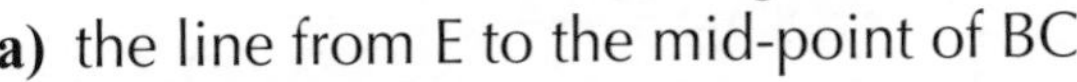

a) the line from E to the mid-point of BC
b) the sloping edge BE.

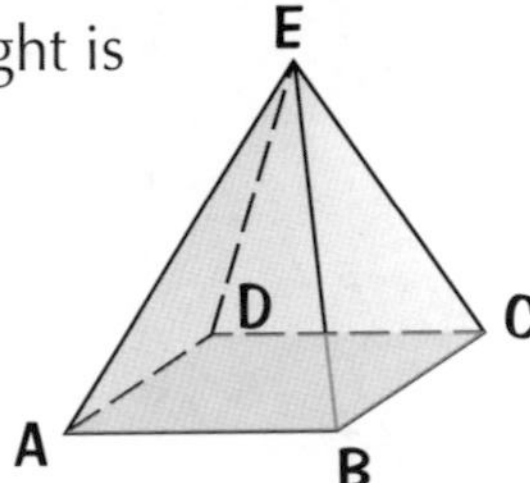

Q3 A rectangular box measures 20 cm by 30 cm by 8 cm. Calculate the lengths of:

a) the diagonal of each rectangular face
b) the diagonal through the centre of the box.

Q4 This glass has a radius of 2.8 cm. The straw in the glass makes an angle of 70° with the base and protrudes 4 cm above the rim.

a) How tall is the glass?
b) How long is the straw?

Q5 A shop sells the three different gift boxes shown on the right. Katie wants to buy the cheapest box that will fit a pen that is 10 cm long. Which box should she buy?

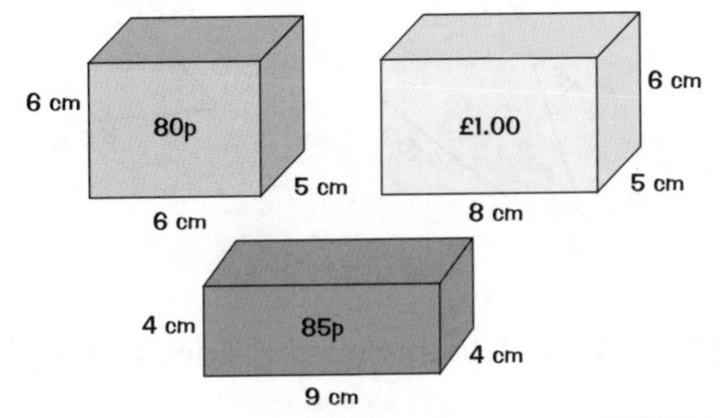

Q6 This cone has a perpendicular height of 9 cm. The centre of the base is O. The slant line from X makes an angle of 23° with the central axis. Calculate:

a) the radius of the base
b) the area of the base
c) the volume of the cone.

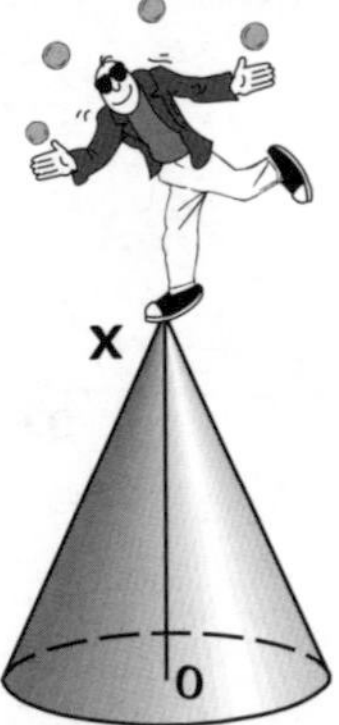

The Sine and Cosine Rules

Make sure you know the Sine Rule and <u>both forms</u> of the Cosine Rule. The one to use depends on which angles and sides you're given.

Q1 Calculate the lengths required to 3 s.f.

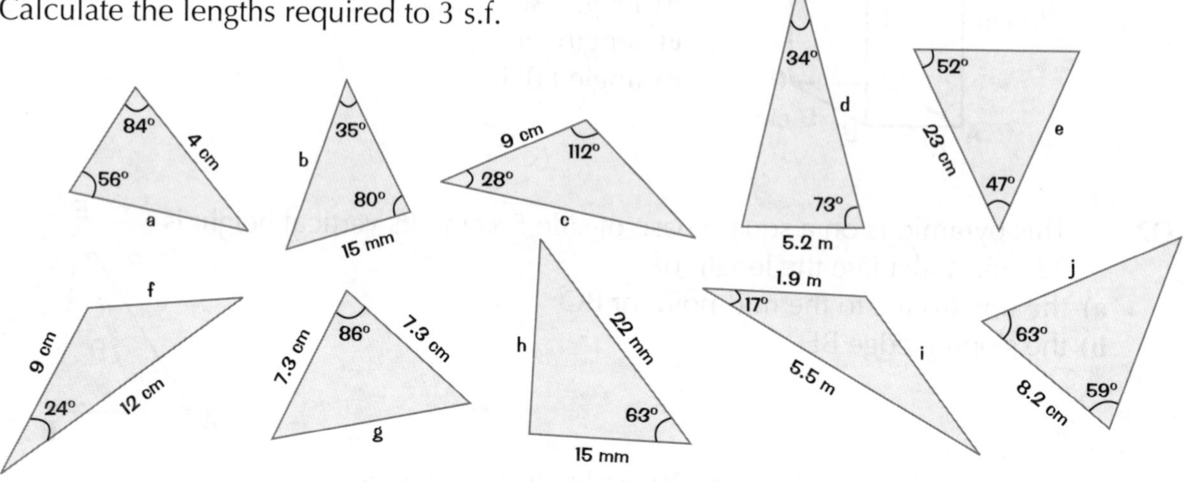

Q2 Calculate the angles required, to the nearest degree.

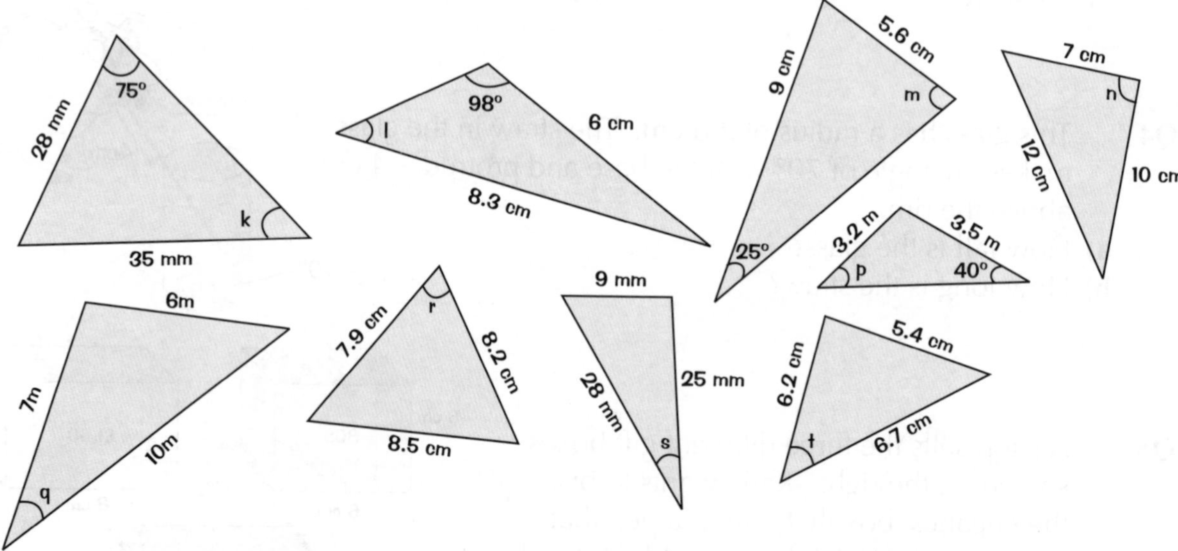

Q3 Calculate the lettered sides and angles.

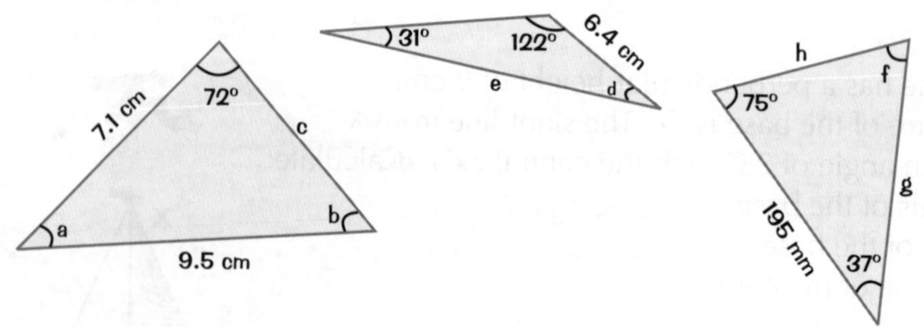

The Sine and Cosine Rules

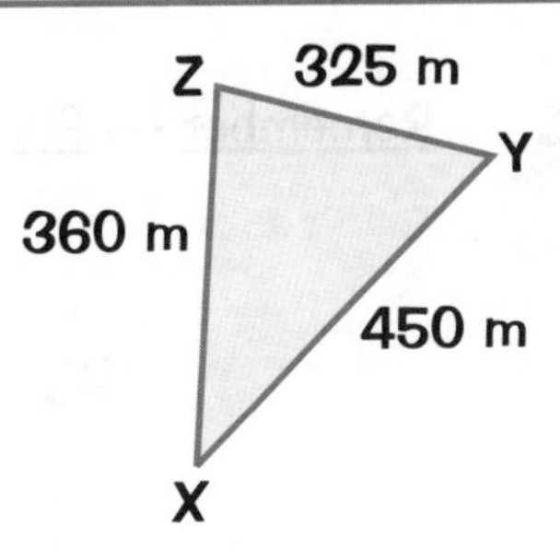

Q4 This field has measurements as shown. Calculate:

a) ∠ZXY

b) ∠XYZ

c) ∠YZX.

Q5 Peter is standing on a bridge over a river. He can see a tree on each bank, one 33 m and the other 35 m away from him. If he looks through an angle of 20° going from one tree to the other, how far apart are the two trees?

Q6 Air traffic control are testing the reliability of their computer software by monitoring two aeroplanes and checking the computer's calculations with their own. If the horizontal distance between the planes drops to 3 miles or less, an alarm should be triggered on the computer. One of the test planes is at a distance of 5 miles from the tower, and on a bearing of 020° from the tower. The second is at a distance of 4.6 miles on a bearing of 034° and the alarm is ringing. Calculate the horizontal distance between the planes and comment on the reliability of the software.

Q7 An aircraft leaves A and flies 257 km to B on a bearing of 257°. It then flies on to C, 215 km away on a bearing of 163° from B. Calculate:

a) ∠ABC

b) distance CA

c) the bearing needed to fly from A direct to C.

Q8 On my clock the hour hand is 5.5 cm, the minute hand 8 cm and the second hand 7 cm, measured from the centre. Calculate the distance between the tips of the:

a) hour and minute hands at 10 o'clock

b) minute and second hands 15 seconds before 20 past the hour

c) hour and minute hands at 1020.

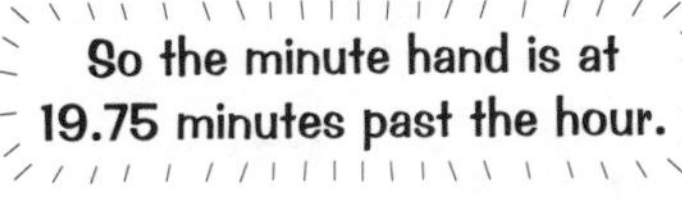

So the minute hand is at
19.75 minutes past the hour.

Q9 A surveyor wants to measure the height of a building. She measures the angle of elevation of the top of the building from the two different positions shown. Calculate the height of the building to the nearest metre.

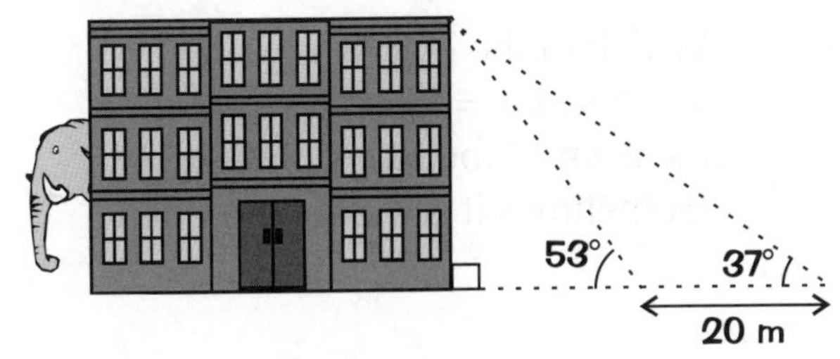

The Graphs of Sin, Cos and Tan

Remember — Sin and Cos only have values between –1 and 1.

Q1 This is the graph of $y = \sin(x)$. Write down the coordinates of the points A, B and C.

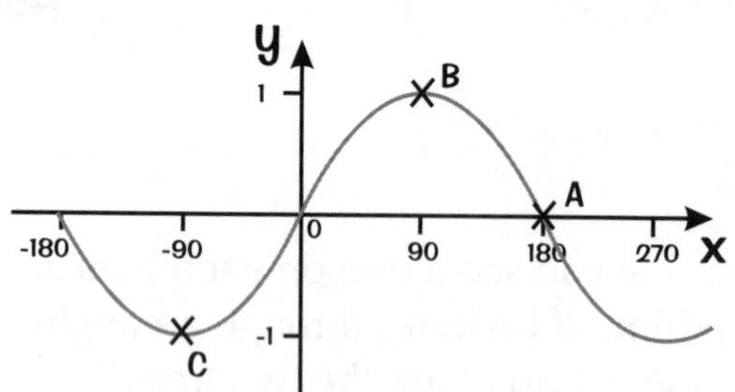

Q2 This is the graph of $y = \cos(x)$. Write down the coordinates of the points D, E, F and G.

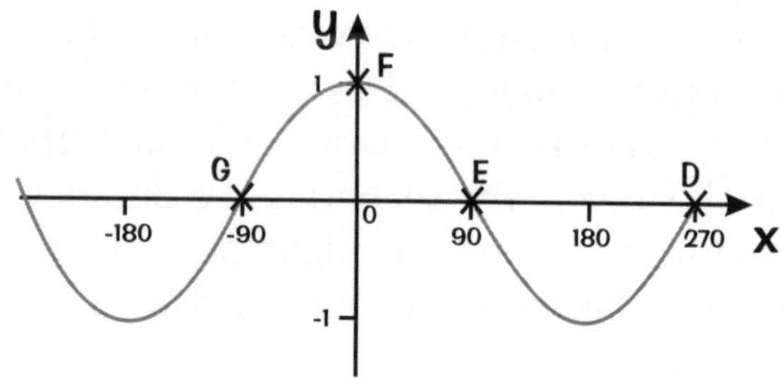

Q3 This is the graph of $y = \tan(x)$. Write down the coordinates of the points H, I and J.

Don't forget — something strange happens with tan at 90°, 270°, 450° etc. — it shoots off to + infinity... still, at least it comes back again (even if it is at – infinity.)

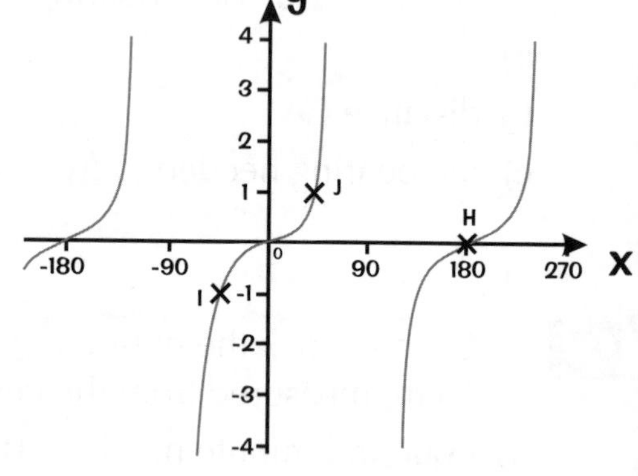

Q4 Which of the graphs $y = \sin(x)$, $y = \cos(x)$, $y = \tan(x)$ go through the points labelled A, B, C, ...J? (Sometimes it is more than one.)

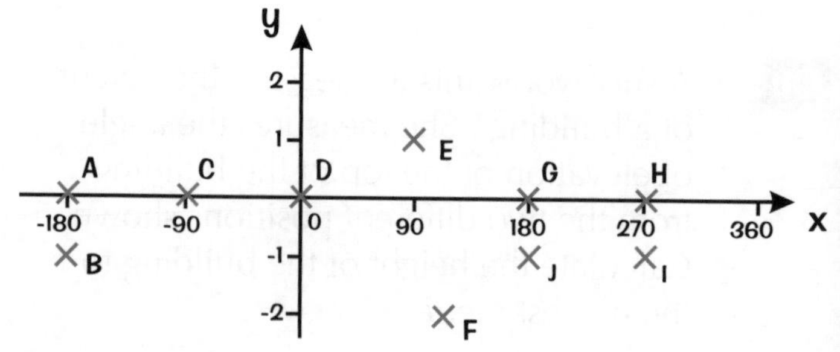

Angles of Any Size

Q1 The graph of $y = \sin(x)$ is shown below for $-720° \leq x \leq 720°$.

Graph of y = sin x -720° ≤ x ≤ 720°

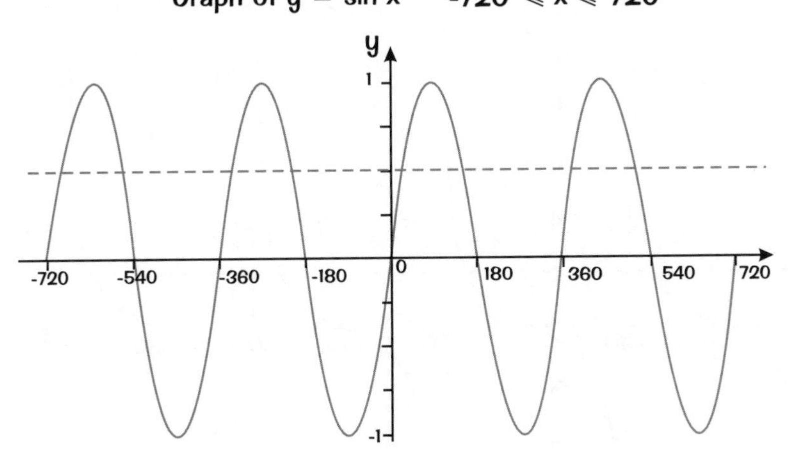

The dotted line drawn at $y = 0.5$ gives values of x as:
–690°, –570°, –330°, –210°, 30°, 150°, 390°, 510°.

Write down all the values of x between –720° and +720°, when:

a) $\sin(x) = -0.5$

b) $\sin(x) = 0.1$

c) $\sin(x) = -0.9$.

Remember — the **Cos** graph is **symmetrical** about the line **x = 0**, but the **Sin** graph **isn't** — it might seem obvious now, but you can guarantee it won't in the Exam.

Q2 The graph of $y = \cos(x)$ is shown below for $-720° \leqslant x \leqslant 720°$.

Graph of y = cos x -720° ≤ x ≤ 720°

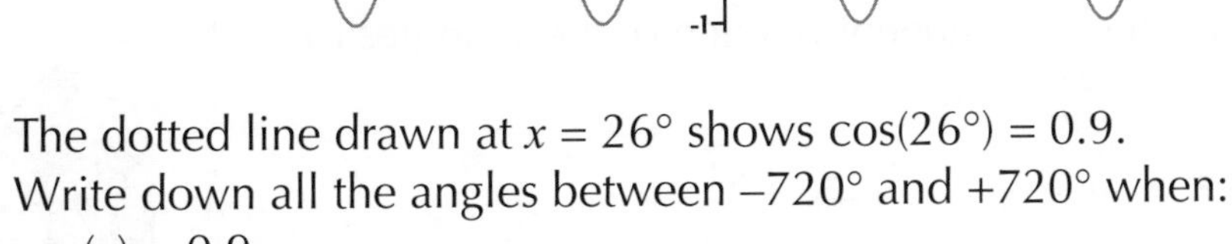

The dotted line drawn at $x = 26°$ shows $\cos(26°) = 0.9$.
Write down all the angles between –720° and +720° when:

a) $\cos(x) = 0.9$

b) $\cos(x) = 0.5$

c) $\cos(x) = -0.6$.

Explain why the positive and negative values are the same for cos, but not for sin.

Angles of Any Size

Q3 The graph of $y = \tan(x)$ is shown below for $-450° \leqslant x \leqslant 450°$.

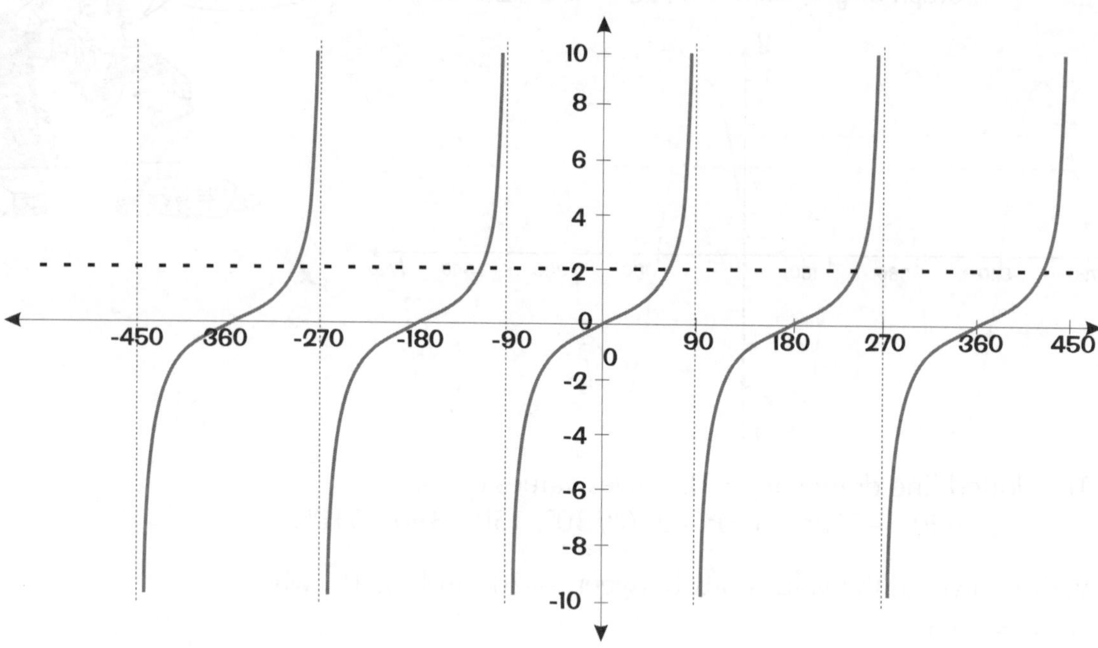

The dotted line drawn where $y = 2$ gives the values of x as:
$-297°$, $-117°$, $63°$, $243°$, $423°$.

Write down all the values of x between $-450° \leqslant x \leqslant 450°$ to the nearest degree when:

a) $\tan(x) = -1$
b) $\tan(x) = 0.5$
c) $\tan(x) = 3$.

Q4 Write down 4 possible values of x, to the nearest degree, if:

a) $\sin(x) = 0.39$
b) $\cos(x) = 0.39$
c) $\tan(x) = -39$.

You've got to know how often these graphs repeat themselves.

Q5 Write down the sine, cosine and tangent of each of these angles to 3 s.f.:

a) 175°
b) –175°
c) 405°
d) –735°.
e) What do you notice about the answers to **a)** and **b)**?
f) Can you explain why this happens?

Loci and Constructions

Don't let a silly word like <u>locus</u> put you off — there are <u>easy marks</u> to be had here, but you've got to do everything neatly, using a pencil, ruler and compasses.

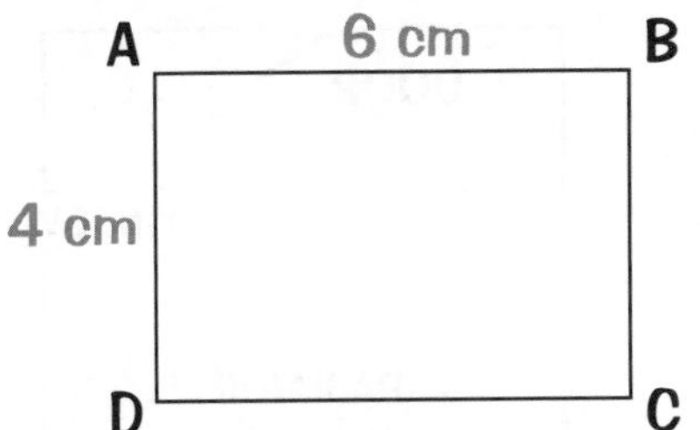

Q1 Inside a 6 cm by 4 cm rectangle:

a) draw the locus of points 5 cm from D

b) draw the locus of points equidistant from A and D

c) indicate by an X, the point inside the rectangle which is 5 cm from D and equidistant from A and D.

Q2 Construct triangle PQR accurately with length PQ = 10.5 cm, angle PQR = 95° and angle RPQ = 32°.

a) Construct the perpendicular bisector of the line PR. Draw in point A where the bisector crosses the line PQ.

b) Bisect angle PRQ. Draw in point B where the bisector crosses the line PQ. Measure the length BA.

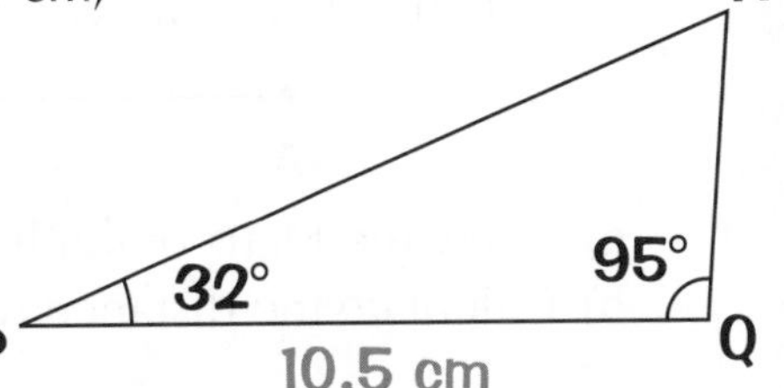

Q3 Omar is doing some garden landscaping. Because of gas and water pipes, he is not allowed to dig anywhere within 3 m of his house.

Using a scale of 1 cm to 1 m, draw a diagram for Omar showing the walls of his house and the area in which he cannot dig.

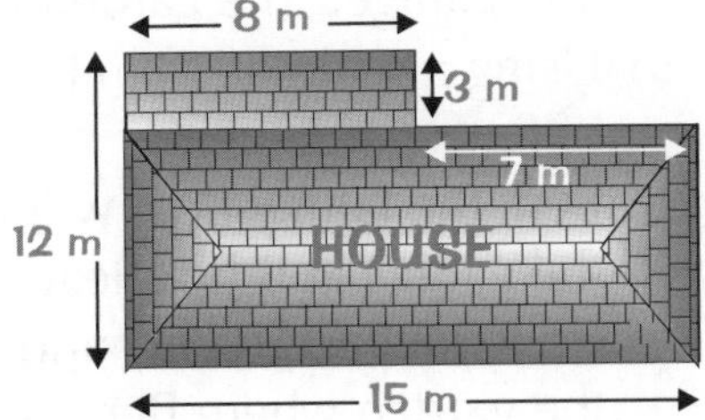

Q4 Construct triangle PQR with length PQ = QR = 11.5 cm and angle PQR = 38°.

a) Construct the bisectors of angles QPR and QRP. Mark the point O where the 2 bisectors cross.

b) With centre O draw the circle which just touches the sides PQ, PR and QR of the triangle. What is the radius of this circle?

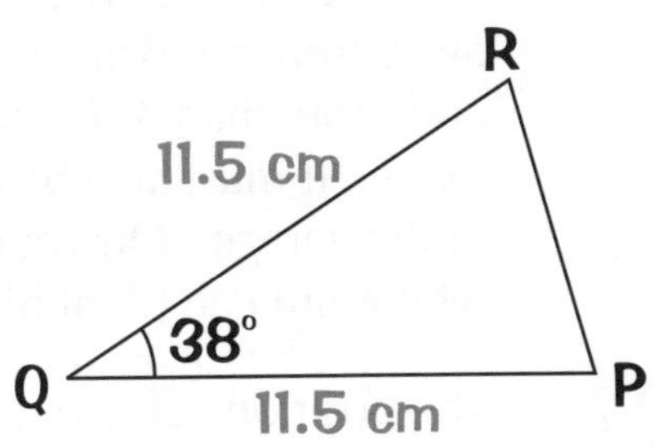

Q5 A and B are 2 points on a straight shore, 4 km apart with A due west of B.

a) Describe the locus of points P such that angle APB equals 90°.

b) Using a scale of 2 cm to 1 km draw an accurate scale diagram showing A, B, the shore line and the locus of P.

Think about your geometry rules.

An outcrop of rock is located on a bearing of 060° from A and 300° from B.

c) Indicate the rock on your diagram. Mark the spot with an X.

d) A ship steaming due east parallel to the shore avoids the rock by following the locus of P. How near does the ship come to the rock?

Loci and Constructions

Just to be really awkward, these points don't always make a nice line — they can cover a whole area... and you're gonna be asked to shade areas containing all the points.

Q6 This is a plan of Simon's room. To keep warm Simon must be within 2 m of the wall with the radiator on. To see out of the window he must be within 1.5 m of the wall containing the window.

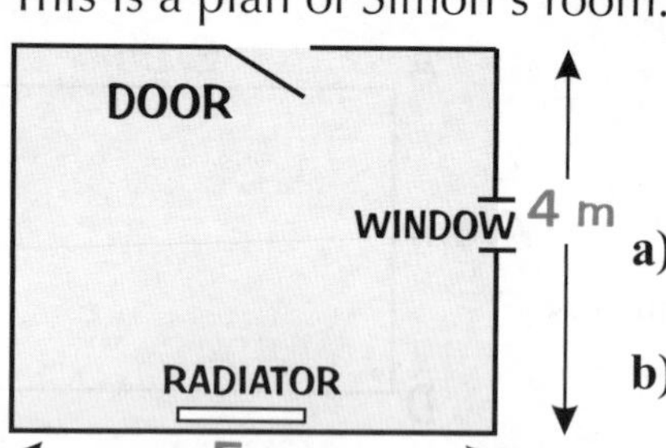

a) Using a scale of 2 cm to 1 m draw a plan of Simon's room.

b) Shade the region in which Simon must be if he is to be warm and see out of the window.

Q7 A running track is designed so that each point on the track is 32.5 m from a fixed line AB which is 100 m long.

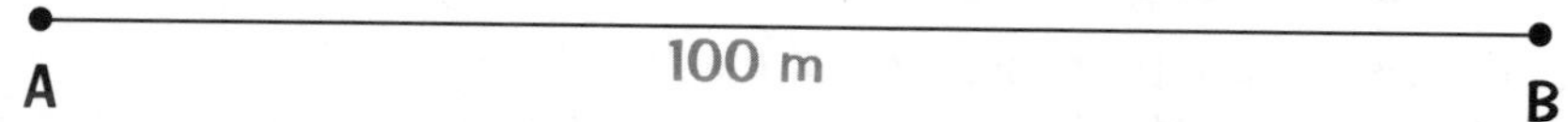

a) Draw the locus of the line.

b) Calculate the distance once round the running track.

Q8 Jim is landscaping his back garden, and has drawn the plan below. Two sides of the garden are bounded by fences and the other sides are bounded by the walls of the house and garage. The garden is in the shape of a rectangle.

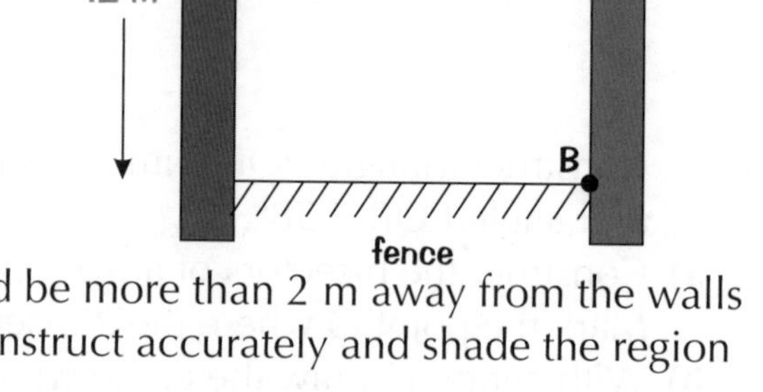

a) Using a scale of 1 cm to 1 m draw a plan of Jim's garden.

b) Ben, the family dog, will be tethered to the garage at B by a lead of length 6 m. Construct accurately and shade the part of the garden where Ben can go.

c) Jim wants to plant a tree in the garden. The tree must be planted more than 5 m away from the walls of the house and more than 4 m away from each fence. It must also be out of reach of Ben, and be more than 2 m away from the walls of the garage. On your plan of the garden, construct accurately and shade the region where Jim can plant his tree.

Q9 The positions of two islands A and B are found from the following information: A is 35 km from a jetty J on a bearing 065°, B is due south of A and on a bearing of 132° from J as shown below.

a) Using a scale of 1 cm to 5 km, draw an accurate plan to show the positions of J, A and B.

b) Find from your drawing the distance in km between the islands A and B.

c) A boat leaves the jetty at 09.00 and reaches A at 11.30. What is its average speed in km/h?

d) A lightship L is 20 km from J, equidistant from A and B and on the same side of J as A and B. Mark L on the drawing.

e) Find the bearing of L from J.

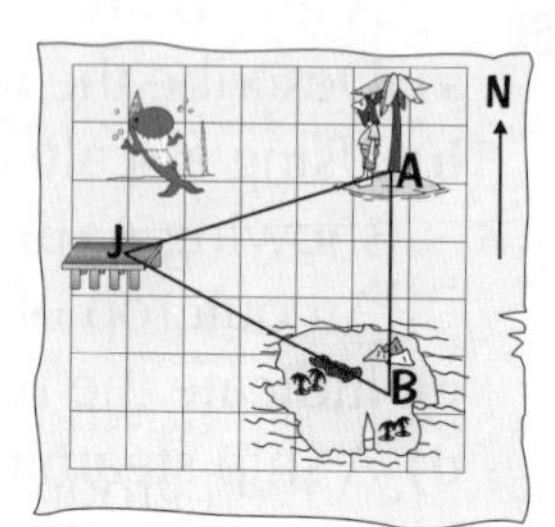

Grouped Frequency Tables

Q1 The speeds of 32 skiers at a certain corner of a downhill course are tabulated below.

Speed (km/h)	$40 \leq s < 45$	$45 \leq s < 50$	$50 \leq s < 55$	$55 \leq s < 60$	$60 \leq s < 65$
Frequency	4	8	10	7	3
Mid-Interval					
Frequency × Mid-Interval					

a) By completing the frequency table, estimate the mean speed.
b) How many skiers were travelling at less than 55 km/h?
c) How many skiers were travelling at 50 km/h or faster?

Q2 The weights in kg of 18 newly felled trees are noted below:
272.7 333.2 251.0 246.5 328.0 259.6 200.2 312.8 344.3
226.8 362.0 348.3 256.1 232.9 309.7 398.0 284.5 327.4

a) Complete the frequency table.

Weight (kg)	Tally	Frequency	Mid-Interval	Frequency × Mid-Interval
$200 \leq w < 250$				
$250 \leq w < 300$				
$300 \leq w < 350$				
$350 \leq w < 400$				

b) Estimate the mean weight using the frequency table.
c) What is the modal group?

Q3 48 numbers are recorded below:

0.057 0.805 0.056 0.979 0.419 0.160 0.534 0.763
0.642 0.569 0.773 0.055 0.349 0.892 0.664 0.136
0.528 0.792 0.085 0.546 0.549 0.908 0.639 0.000
0.614 0.478 0.421 0.472 0.292 0.579 0.542 0.356
0.070 0.890 0.883 0.333 0.033 0.323 0.544 0.668
0.094 0.049 0.049 0.999 0.632 0.700 0.983 0.356

a) Transfer the data into the frequency table.

Number	$0 \leqslant n < 0.2$	$0.2 \leqslant n < 0.4$	$0.4 \leqslant n < 0.6$	$0.6 \leqslant n < 0.8$	$0.8 \leqslant n < 1$
Tally					
Frequency					
Mid-Interval					
Frequency × Mid-Interval					

b) Write down the modal class(es).
c) Which group contains the median?
d) Estimate the mean value.

Cumulative Frequency

Q1 Using the cumulative frequency curve, read off the:

a) median
b) lower quartile
c) upper quartile
d) interquartile range.

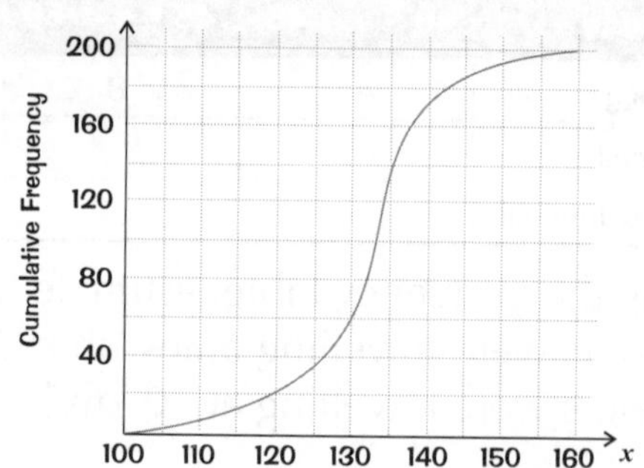

Q2 The number of passengers using a bus service each day has been recorded over a 4-week period. The data is presented in the table below:

No. passengers	$0 \le n < 50$	$50 \le n < 100$	$100 \le n < 150$	$150 \le n < 200$	$200 \le n < 250$	$250 \le n < 300$
Frequency	2	7	10	5	3	1
Cumulative Frequency						
Mid-Interval						
Frequency × Mid-Interval						

A mean passenger

a) By completing the table, estimate the mean number of passengers.
b) By plotting a cumulative frequency curve, determine the median value.
c) What is the modal group?

With cumulative frequency you always plot the highest value from each class.

Q3 40 pupils have taken an exam and their marks are recorded in a frequency table.

Mark (%)	$0 \leqslant m < 20$	$20 \leqslant m < 40$	$40 \leqslant m < 60$	$60 \leqslant m < 80$	$80 \leqslant m < 100$
Frequency	2	12	18	5	3
Cumulative Frequency					

a) Complete the table and plot the cumulative frequency curve.
b) What is the value of the lower quartile?
c) What is the interquartile range?
d) What is the median mark?

Cumulative Frequency

Q4 One hundred scores for a board game are presented in the table below.

Score	31 ≤ s < 41	41 ≤ s < 51	51 ≤ s < 61	61 ≤ s < 71	71 ≤ s < 81	81 ≤ s < 91	91 ≤ s < 101
Frequency	4	12	21	32	19	8	4
Cumulative Frequency							

a) What is the modal group?
b) Which group contains the median score?
c) By plotting the cumulative frequency curve determine the actual value of the median score.
d) Find the interquartile range.

Q5 The following frequency table gives the distribution of the lives of electric bulbs.

a) Complete the frequency table.

Life (hours)	Frequency	Cumulative Frequency
900 ≤ L < 1000	10	
1000 ≤ L < 1100	12	
1100 ≤ L < 1200	15	
1200 ≤ L < 1300	18	
1300 ≤ L < 1400	22	
1400 ≤ L < 1500	17	
1500 ≤ L < 1600	14	
1600 ≤ L < 1700	9	

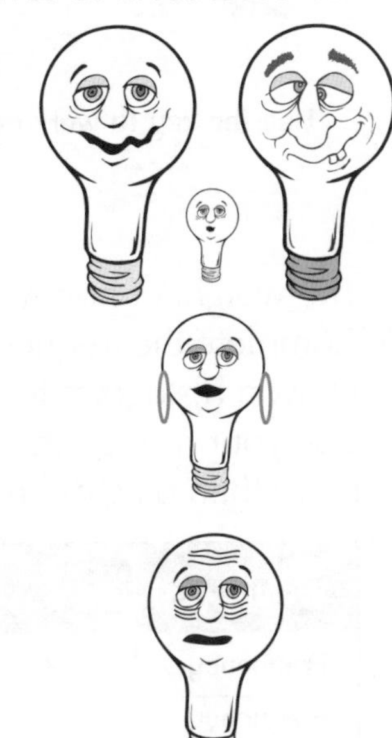

b) Which group contains the median value?
c) By drawing the cumulative frequency curve, find the actual value of the median.
d) Determine values for the upper and lower quartiles.

Q6 30 pupils recorded the time taken (minutes : seconds) to boil some water.
Here are their results:

2:37 2:37 3:17 3:30 2:45 2:13 3:18 3:12 3:38 3:29
3:04 3:24 4:13 3:01 3:11 2:33 3:37 4:24 3:59 3:11
3:22 3:13 2:57 3:12 3:07 4:17 3:31 3:42 3:51 3:24

a) By using a tally, transfer the data into the frequency table.
b) Draw the cumulative frequency curve.

Time	2:00 ⩽ t < 2:30	2:30 ⩽ t < 3:00	3:00 ⩽ t < 3:30	3:30 ⩽ t < 4:00	4:00 ⩽ t < 4:30
Tally					
Frequency					
Cumulative Frequency					

c) Using your graph, read off the median and the upper and lower quartiles.
d) What is the interquartile range?

Histograms and Frequency Density

It's the <u>size that counts</u>... You've got to look at the <u>area</u> of the bars to find the frequency. That means looking at the <u>width</u> as well as the height.

Q1 The Bog Snorkelling Appreciation Society conducts a survey on the ages of all their members. The histogram below shows the age distribution of the people surveyed. The Society organises a 'Seniors' bog snorkelling event for members aged 60 or older. Use the graph to estimate the maximum number of people that might take part.

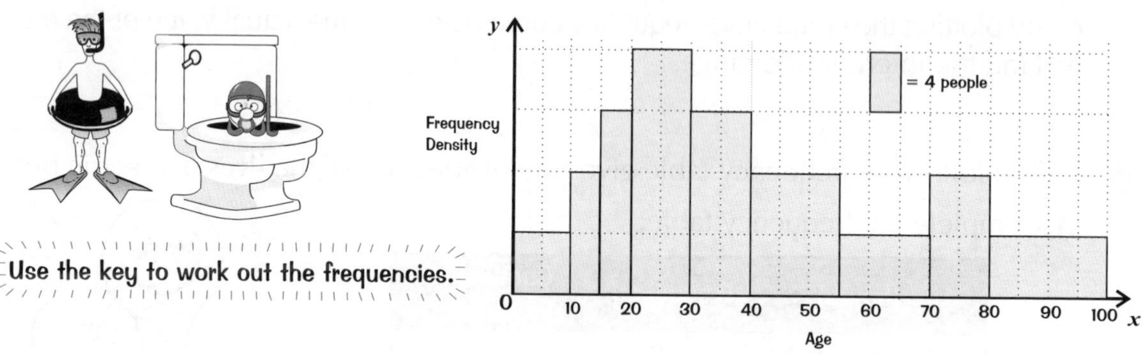

Q2 The weight of honey collected from several beehives is tabulated below.

a) Complete the frequency table by calculating the frequency densities.

b) Draw a histogram to represent this data.

c) Use your histogram to estimate the number of beehives that produced more than 6 kg of honey.

Weight (kg)	$0 \le w < 2$	$2 \le w < 4$	$4 \le w < 7$	$7 \le w < 9$	$9 \le w < 15$
Frequency	3	2	6	9	12
Frequency density					

Q3 Match the histograms to their corresponding cumulative frequency curves.

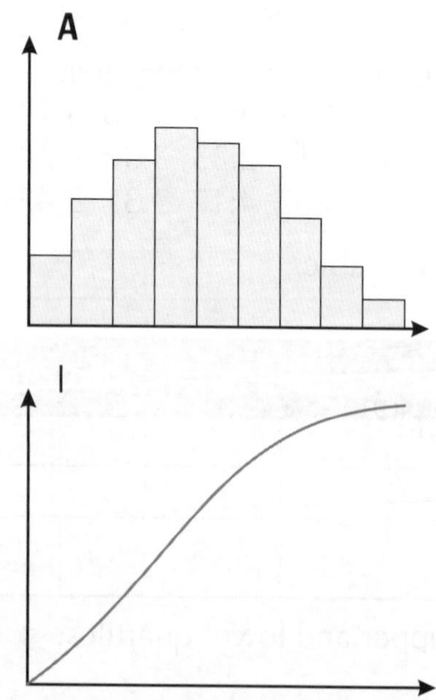

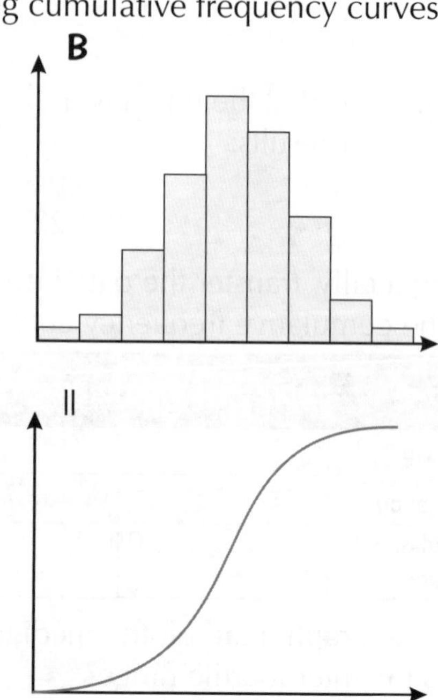

Histograms and Frequency Density

Know your shapes — they're bound to ask you what different-shaped graphs mean, so get learning.

Q4 A group of sixth formers took part in a survey to see how much time they spent watching TV each week.

a) Complete the table by filling in the frequency density column.
b) How many students took part in the survey?
c) Represent the data as a histogram.
d) Estimate the number of students that watch more than 7, but less than 13 hours each week.

No. of hours	Frequency	Frequency density
$0 \le h < 1$	6	
$1 \le h < 3$	13	
$3 \le h < 5$	15	
$5 \le h < 8$	9	
$8 \le h < 10$	23	
$10 \le h < 15$	25	
$15 \le h < 20$	12	

Q5 Below are two histograms — one shows the weights of a sample of 16 year olds, and the other shows the weights of a sample of 1 kg bags of sugar. Say which is which.

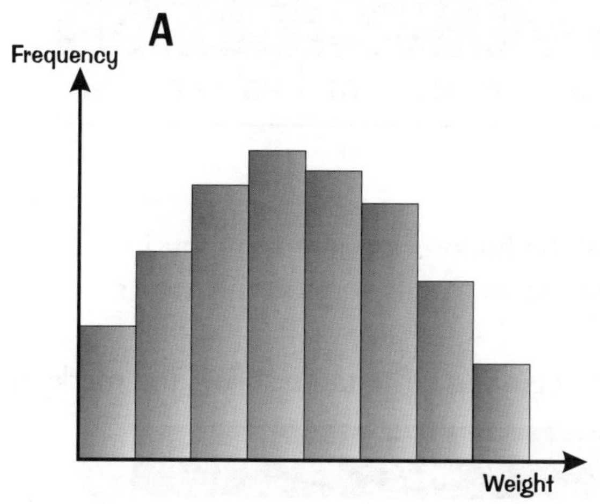

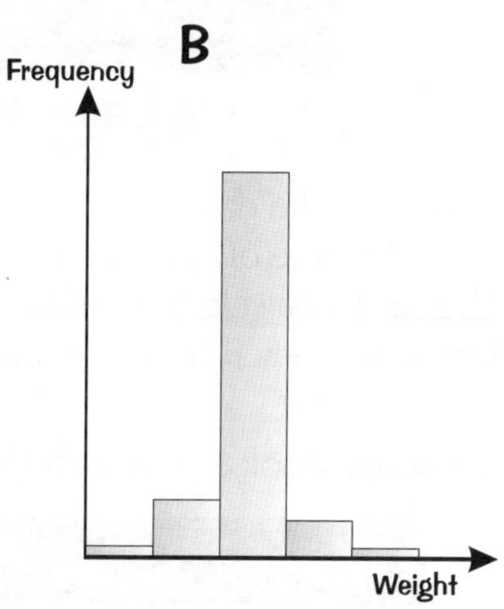

Q6 A local newspaper employee has collected data on the salaries of 100 people living in the area. His data is shown in the table below.

Salary (£1000s)	$0 \le s < 10$	$10 \le s < 20$	$20 \le s < 30$	$30 \le s < 40$	$40 \le s < 50$
Frequency	10	25	42	20	3
Frequency Density					

a) Complete the table and draw a histogram to show the data.
b) The newspaper prints this histogram alongside the one shown on the right. It represents data from an identical survey done 10 years earlier. Write a comment comparing current salaries and those from 10 years ago.

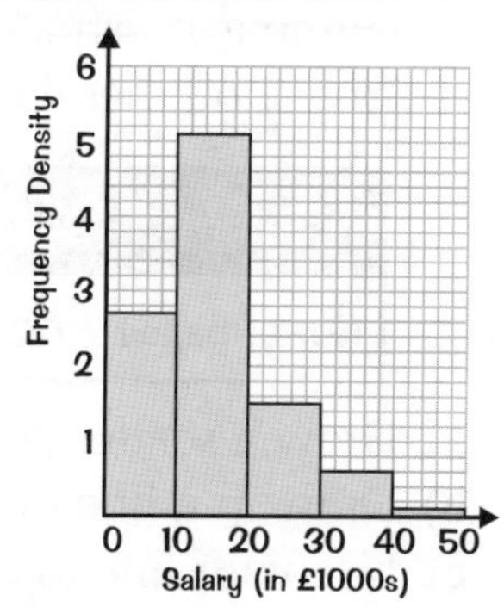

Scatter Diagrams

A <u>SCATTER DIAGRAM</u> is just a load of points on a graph that <u>end up in a bit of a mess</u>, rather than in a nice line or curve. There's a fancy word to say how much of a mess they're in — it's <u>CORRELATION</u>.

Q1 Match the following diagrams with the most appropriate descriptive label.

Labels: (P) Strong positive correlation
(Q) Exact negative correlation
(R) Little or no correlation
(S) Moderate negative correlation
(T) Medium correlation
(U) Exact positive correlation.

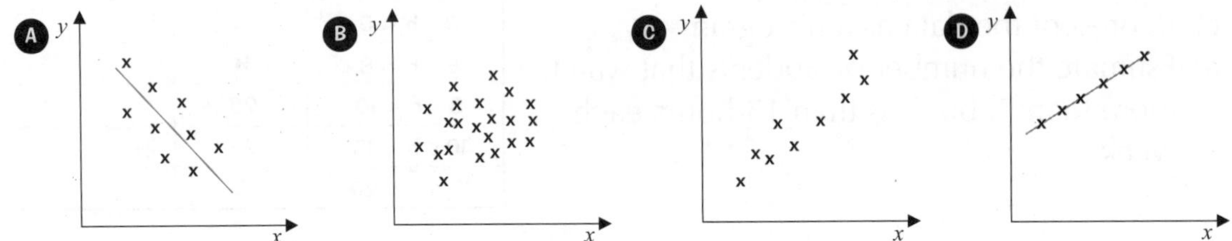

Q2 The examination results (%) for a class of students for 2 exams are shown in the table.

Physics	97	61	36	56	48	84	83	79	26	66
Chemistry	98	65	49	66	60	88	87	85	43	78

a) Represent the data with a scatter graph.
b) State the type of correlation, if any.
c) The students' science teacher thinks that the better a student is at physics, the better they'll be at chemistry. Do the exam results support this view?

Q3 10 people took 2 exams in Welding for Beginners. The table shows the marks obtained.

Candidate	1	2	3	4	5	6	7	8	9	10
Exam 1 (%)	85	30	55	10	40	20	0	95	65	40
Exam 2 (%)	70	25	50	15	70	25	5	80	60	35

a) Draw a scatter graph representing this information.
b) Draw a line of best fit.
c) Clive only sat the first exam, obtaining a mark of 50%. Use your scatter graph to estimate the mark that he might have achieved if he had sat the second exam.

Q4 Janine is convinced that the more expensive cookery books contain more pages. To test out her theory, she has compiled this table:

Price	£4.25	£5.00	£4.75	£6.25	£7.50	£8.25	£4.75	£5.00	£6.75	£3.25	£3.75
No. of pages	172	202	118	184	278	328	158	138	268	84	98

a) Draw a scatter graph to represent this information.
b) Draw in a line of best fit.
c) Use your line to estimate the price of a book containing 250 pages.